Other Books by Jennifer Griffin:

Understanding Your Child as a Spiritual Gift

"What an elegant theory!...This is the only convincing motivation I've come across to practice mindfulness. It is a quick, easy read, and is empowering for parents." *Psychiatrist—Aviva Goldman, M.D.*

"... presents an ingenious approach to navigating the extremely complex emotional journey on which all parents embark. Thought-provoking and engagingly written, Griffin delineates an intriguing hypothesis...Chock-full of practical suggestions for parents..." *Psychologist—Jennifer D. Vidas, Ph.D.*

"After a particularly harrowing day with my two boys, I read this whole book cover to cover during a long bath...helping me understand all of our family relationships better, and have another tool when things are especially difficult."*Anhonestmom.com—Stephanie Mackley*

"...gives you understanding, confidence & is easy to read."*—TheBabySpot.ca*

"This book is a Wonder...a treasure chest of spiritual tools we need to heal ourselves and our children." *Mother of 4—Janny Castillo*

"...was a breath of fresh air, AND a wake up call!... love her easy to read and very entertaining real life experiences...Should be required reading for every teacher, therapist, and parent!" *Author of Healing Mama—Amanda Nube*

Understanding Morning Sickness as a Gift:

An Introspective Story of Healing and Hope from a Hyperemesis Gravidarum Survivor

Jennifer Griffin, MS
Spiritual Gift Institute
Berkley, CA

****

Praise for
Understanding Morning Sickness as a Gift

"I was really caught off guard by debilitating morning sickness with my second pregnancy, and *Understanding Morning Sickness as a Gift* was a significant resource for me as I struggled to try and balance raising my son and working during this time. Griffin's tips on natural remedies in combination with medication made it so I could continue to function (eating a protein heavy diet as she suggested really helped me). Further, this book helped me realize I was not alone in what felt like a very isolating experience. I will keep this book on hand as a resource for friends and myself in the future!" —*Lisa, HG survivor*

"This is an absolute must read for families touched by HG. Spiritually awakening and empowering, this is a journey that gathered vast knowledge, acceptance and healing on every level. This isn't just a personal account of one mother's journey with HG, it's a healing survival guide for the body, mind and soul for before, during and after." —*Emma, mother of 4 and doula*

"True to form, Griffin ties together all the pieces of real life events, spiritual wisdom and insight into how we work physically and emotionally in this fascinating momento."—*Karen, mother of 2*

Contents

Preface

Although my struggle with hyperemesis gravidarum (HG) fueled the momentum for this project, as I put the book together I realized how much the sensitive subjects of sexual abuse and domestic violence stood out. I want to forewarn readers about these disheartening topics and encourage you, the reader, to skip over the parts that are uncomfortable. I know at times I am triggered when I read about sexual abuse; however, I feel there is so much silence around the experience. When we break the silence and share our stories, we collectively heal. As our voices are heard, we stand up to our abusers and those bystanders who did nothing to rescue us. The more we do this, the less power their actions have and the more educated people become. Together we create an environment where we stand united, refusing to tolerate the silence any longer.

This silence also pervades and perpetuates the experience of domestic violence, which is another potentially disturbing topic mentioned in this book. I discuss these subjects because of how important they were to my healing. Even though these issues were prominent in my recovery journey, every woman with HG has not experienced these issues. Although there are many similarities among HG survivors, each of our experiences is unique—reminding us that we need to discover our individual path to healing.

Many HG survivors push through much more severe HG than I did. I admire you because I cannot imagine it being any worse. You are true champions. I am not sure why my HG was not severe, but part of me thinks I had already experienced a lot of chronic pain. Once my body started to speak to me, I learned to listen and basically cancelled my life. I know everyone does not share this privilege, but many of us have more of an opportunity than we realize. I dropped out of graduate school and after so many HG pregnancies chose to leave the rat race of costly vacations, remodeled houses, professional landscaping and cleaning services to focus solely on raising my family simply.

If you have ever struggled with severe HG, I imagine this book may frustrate you. For example, I have seen critical remarks by HG survivors disregarding *Managing Morning Sickness* by Miriam Erick: a book to which I am ever grateful for sorting out the different characteristics of HG and giving me specific acupuncture points to try. There was hardly any information available during my first HG pregnancy, and Erick was one of the first authors to provide a resource for pregnant women about this subject. I was so appreciative to see the progress from her initial book and her willingness to keep trying to discover the causes and cures for this treacherous illness.

As many women know, morning sickness does not only happen in the morning and often lasts all day and much beyond the first trimester. Therefore, I use the term pregnancy sickness throughout this book to more accurately describe the experience. Pregnancy sickness is an unexpected adjustment for many women, and an unbelievable battle for women with HG. Women are expected to carry on like nothing has changed and continue without pause in their already stressful lives. For women with HG, this is impossible. The specific ideas and tips discussed in this book will be most valuable to those plagued with moderate to severe nausea and vomiting in pregnancy, as well as those with mild to moderate HG.

The general healing techniques mentioned will also benefit those individuals with other medical conditions that seem to have no specific cure—helping to resolve the underlying spiritual and emotional issues that contribute to a variety of diseases, especially chronic ones. The multiple alternative healing techniques discussed in chapters 8 and 9 have potential to heal anyone. With this book, I hope to touch someone, somewhere and make their intense journey a little more manageable.

In trying to alleviate my HG, I wrote my Master's thesis about it, advocating for more social support for HG survivors and suggested a website for communication. A year after my graduation, the HER Foundation fortunately created a website to dispel many of the myths about this illness, supplying the desperately needed resources and connection for women worldwide. As the Internet exploded, more women shared their stories and The Pink Stork developed an HG protocol providing healing for the whole body.

On the following pages, I share my recollections of surviving HG on and off for more than ten years transforming my unresolved emotional pain into creative joy. Finally, I healed in my fifth pregnancy as I discovered Mayan abdominal massage for a tight diaphragm, and retried unsuccessful past therapies, such as home treatments of cranial sacral and acupuncture, as well as medical marijuana. In my last pregnancy, my diet consisted of barley tea in between meals of large amounts of protein, such as three hamburgers and three hot dogs for breakfast alone, while shunning carbohydrates.

The most crucial long-term healing occurred in between my pregnancies. Most importantly, I left a domestically violent marriage, became sober, completed ten sessions of Zen trigger muscle fascia release, did a liver cleanse, deepened my spirituality and examined my perfectionistic tendencies and unresolved sexual abuse issues. Just as there are many causes for HG, there is no one cure. A combination of factors appears to cause HG, requiring a unique collection of solutions for HG to resolve. My wish for you is to discover and welcome your magical formula for healing.

Understanding Morning Sickness as a Gift:

****

An Introspective Story of Healing and Hope from a Hyperemesis Gravidarum Survivor

1

The Beginning of My HG Journey

"Excuse me, are you okay?" asked the flight attendant kindly after the plane had landed in Australia and everyone else had departed the aircraft.

"I don't know." I struggled to barely mumble as the severe nausea caused me to collapse into the aisle.

"Do you have a medical condition?" she inquired.

"Not that I know of." I answered weakly.

The nausea was so debilitating I was taken off the airplane in a wheelchair. I was traveling alone and thought I was dying—never had I experienced such excruciating nausea. Unbeknownst to me, this would become a regular part of my life for the next ten years of childbearing.

My Australian host was out of town on a business trip and had sent his friend to pick me up at the airport. I seldom feel embarrassed, but here I was collapsed in a wheelchair not wanting to alarm this stranger who was doing a favor for my friend. Awkwardly I tried to explain what was happening, which was especially challenging because I had no clue what to say. Thankfully, we ruled out doctors and hospitals, and I went back to my friend's empty house and I slept the rest of the day and through the night.

Fortunately, the nausea subsided after a day and I spent the rest of my vacation enjoying Australia. After I flew home, the nausea returned with a vengeance and I started vomiting everything I ate— eventually realizing I was pregnant.

A couple of weeks later I was diagnosed with hyperemesis

gravidarum (HG): a severe type of nausea and vomiting during pregnancy. The condition only affects one to two percent of pregnancies and is characterized by severe nausea and vomiting that requires some sort of medical intervention, such as intravenous fluids (IV) for rehydration, medication to stop the vomiting and in the worst cases, tube feeding.

Before my HG diagnosis, I sat in the doctor's office with a positive home pregnancy test vomiting my guts out while mentioning to the nurse I was pregnant. She half ignored me saying I would need to take another pregnancy test.

Take note of how the medical staff disempowered me at the very beginning of my pregnancy. There was no joy, only doubt and disempowerment. This was my first experience with the "experts" as a mother and already they had set me up to fail. The staff was not consciously doing this—regrettably this is a major flaw in our healthcare system. I was beginning to doubt my body and my ability to take my health in my own hands and successfully take a home pregnancy test. My subconscious started to file away thoughts about how would I manage another living being if I cannot even get this right.

The nurse mechanically instructed me to pee in a cup. After reading the results, she radically changed her demeanor and re-entered the room smiling excitedly, "Congratulations, you're pregnant!"

"Thanks, I already figured that out," I grumbled under my breath.

The doctor forewarned me to hold off the prenatal vitamins if I was too nauseous, sending me on my way, claiming this was just normal pregnancy sickness as everyone else seemed to be commenting. Elders, especially, frequently remarked with a smirk, "Oh, that is just how pregnancy is."

No one had cautioned me to record how much and what I vomited, leading me to believe it was normal to vomit several times a day, even when the bile came up. I continued to go to work each day because I was at the tail end of launching a new social services program and could not stand the thought of watching it fall apart if I did not see it through: a pattern I would eventually change, putting others before myself.

Since I had stopped eating and drinking because everything that went in ended up coming out the wrong way, I surprised myself when I vomited so much liquid it filled a five quart cooking pot—wondering to myself *how was that possible if I have not eaten or drunk for days?* Just when I thought there was nothing left inside of me, loads of bile burned through my esophagus.

I cringed feeling like a failure, as I finally called in sick to work, worrying about how my clients might lose the housing we had worked so hard to secure. I phoned my doctor who told me to go immediately to the hospital. I whimpered that I did not have a ride because my now ex-husband, Dimitri, had refused to call in sick to work. She screamed at me to take a cab, but I could not find any money. I did not even have the energy to argue with either of them so I just lay there wondering how to help myself.

Eventually, I pointed out to Dimitri that he had never taken any job seriously. He had rarely worked outside of the house because his main source of income was dealing drugs, and when he did actually have a "real" job, he could only keep the job for a maximum of two weeks. His friends actually used to take bets on how many days, sometimes hours, he could last on a new job.

This confrontation somehow motivated him to contact a couple of friends. Finally, one of his pot customers hesitantly agreed to drive me to the emergency room. There I received IV fluids, was diagnosed with HG and prescribed the anti-emetic, Compazine, for the nausea and vomiting.

In the emergency room, I was feeling at death's door when the doctor ordered an ultrasound to rule out a hydatidaform molar pregnancy, which often causes excessive vomiting. Unable to hold down any liquids, the doctor devised a plan that seemed awful—catheterizing me to fill my bladder to increase the contrast of the ultrasound. I could not even look at people much less have them touch me without feeling violently nauseous. I begged them not to do it and suggested that after I was hydrated I may be able to hold down enough water. The nurse ignored me and forced a catheter in me. I survived but not without feeling tremendously more nauseous.

Suffering with the unbearable nausea, I barely registered the great news when the doctor found the baby's heartbeat and ruled out a hydatidaform molar pregnancy. Since the ultrasound was done, I pleaded with them to remove the catheter and start the IV fluids. Multiple staff members claimed there was no one available to extract the catheter. I was extremely uncomfortable and aggravated they were treating me on their schedule without regard to my intense pain and discomfort. I insisted they take the catheter out now. They refused. I started screaming I would pull out the catheter myself, and voilà, someone appeared instantly to remove it. Finally, they gave me an IV and I slowly began to feel slightly alive again, and I went home naively hopeful the Compazine would rescue me.

A few days later I started losing muscle control of my face and neck. I was scared shitless and had no idea what was going on. Once more, no one had warned me about this possible side effect of Compazine. First it began with my tongue sticking itself in and out. Part of me thought I must be making this up, but then it continued to happen over and over again. I tried all sorts of things to control it. Nothing worked. This was frightening and bizarre so I called my doctor's office. The staff suggested I come in, mentioning nothing about what could be happening.

As I was waiting in the office, my neck began to cramp as the rest of my body tightened, suddenly my head jerked backward and froze for a minute before releasing. Then this cycle happened again and again. It would not stop; it was terrifyingly painful. I started freaking out and crying. A nurse yelled at me, scaring me even more and ignored my pleas to tell me what was happening. Panicking, I could not calm down. *Why wouldn't they tell me what was going on and make it stop? Were they yelling at me because they did not know what to do and were afraid this would keep happening to me? Was this the new state of my life?* Finally, one nurse told me I was having a dystonic reaction to the Compazine, which would be easily alleviated with a shot of Benadryl. In the meantime, I kept suffering through this reaction wondering why I could not receive the shot right now. Eventually, I was given the shot and sent to the hospital for IV Benadryl.

Dimitri appeared at the hospital and began yelling. He screamed about how he did not want to be at the hospital because this was interfering with his customers getting the pot they wanted. I was having trouble sympathizing with him and his customers right now. In retrospect, there was so much this HG was trying to teach me and I was failing to listen.

At the time, I also failed to realize Dimitri's actions constituted domestic violence. Even though I had received numerous domestic violence trainings for various social service jobs, I did not recognize the signs directly in front of me as a part of my life. Because I tend to be outspoken and express myself, I was appalled to learn how powerful denial can be. I thought my expressiveness had made me immune to using this powerful coping mechanism. Upon reflection, denial played a large role in covering up my sexual abuse memories and allowing me to enter into this domestically violent relationship.

Sadly, I had ignored the slamming of Dimitri's hands on the counter while he projected his insecurities on me, yelling at me for being so fucked up. I downplayed the numerous times he drove wildly with his foot pounding alternatively on the gas and brake to scare me, his constant destruction of my favorite pieces of small furniture, and the intimidating body stances where he would back me into a corner glaring at me. He had hit a girlfriend in the past, but I naively believed because he had never hit me this was not domestic violence.

Thirty minutes after getting to the hospital, Dimitri said he was too exhausted from all the yelling and told me he had to leave because he could not wait around for this any longer. Dimitri left and I stayed by myself to finish the IV fluids and IV Benadryl. Even in the few days since my last visit, I was dehydrated again. Not only did the Compazine cause this horrendous reaction, it was also ineffective in controlling the nausea and vomiting. Then a kind doctor came in to talk to me because he was studying dystonic reactions and could not figure out why some people had it and others did not. He explained that many pharmaceuticals caused this type of reaction— sometimes suddenly producing a reaction even if the patient had been taking a medication for years without any problems.

At home I smoked pot since Dimitri had an abundant supply as a dealer. Erroneously, I had imagined it would ease the nausea; it did not. Later, I learned there were specific strains of marijuana formulated into tinctures designed to ease the nausea. In my fifth and last pregnancy, I tried a specific tincture that became a vital part of my treatment plan.

As I continued to look for solutions, I found a small amount of relief from eating meat. I was shocked when I devoured and held down ten pieces of Kentucky fried chicken after being unable to fully digest anything for over two weeks. Eating these remarkable amounts of chicken was also highly unexpected because I had been a vegetarian for the past nine years until that feast.

Even with the added meat, the nausea continued to be out of control so I remained in an absolutely dark room, battling the agonizing nausea.

"Shut the curtains, now!"

"The curtains are shut."

"No, they are not completely shut! Look at that the sliver of light coming through there. Any light makes my nausea go even more through the roof. Then I start vomiting and can't stop."

Controlling the light contained my nausea, keeping me in a state of misery instead of slamming me into an unbearable zone of existence. In addition to light, I had to control if people talked to me or I smelled any food, especially coffee and eggs. It took tremendous effort to manage my environment and survive the overwhelming nausea and vomiting. I spent the next ten years trying to figure out what did and did not affect the nausea—becoming a nausea expert for myself while I searched for answers to why this was happening to me.

In retrospect, I believe my intense reaction to the light and any stimulation was due in part to me reliving the trauma from childhood sexual abuse that had set the stage for me to develop my rigid perfectionism. As I healed piece by piece with each pregnancy, I was able to tolerate a little more light through the cracks as I slowly learned I did not have to control my environment to be safe.

This illness threw me back into the suppressed feelings that had been too intense to experience while I was being abused. Now was my time to experience them and let them go forever. Having another being growing inside reminded me unconsciously of the physical violation I had experienced during my abuse.

After the Compazine fiasco, I vowed to never ever become pregnant again. This shattered my dreams because all I had ever wanted was children and as many as possible. I could not imagine tolerating this experience ever again and I was only eight weeks pregnant. *How was I even going to get through this one?* I counted the minutes each day promising myself I only have to do this once in my life, repeatedly telling myself I know I can make it through this and how this is all I have ever wanted.

Around twelve weeks, I started to feel better and I returned to work, feeling beat up and exhausted. The next weekend, I started to cramp and bleed, followed by contractions every twenty minutes. I ended up having a nine-hour, textbook labor with contractions progressing to ten minutes, five minutes then one minute apart. After I birthed Marley in a bowl on my bathroom floor, I went to tell Dimitri. Within five minutes, I had another contraction and ran back to the bathroom to birth the placenta. Marley was only one and a quarter inches long, yet I could count all his fingers and toes. I could not believe how developed the baby was and how much my body knew what to do as I had labored. Simultaneously, I was devastated and in awe at this incredibly sad, yet powerful experience.

I had just promised myself I would never become pregnant again, then I felt I had to do it again as soon as possible. *No!!!! I don't have it in me to repeat this experience, yet I cannot go on until I have a baby in my arms. How can this be? Where can I go from here?*

My faith in doctors continued to erode when the office called and insisted I bring Marley to the lab for genetic testing, which they promised would help me get pregnant again and carry a baby to full term. Not giving it much thought, I did what they told me without question. I obediently dropped off the blood-filled, blue-covered round Pyrex dish, the container in which I had birthed Marley and his placenta, at the doctor's office, without knowing this would be the last time I would see him. Several weeks passed before receiving the useless results that only verified I had been pregnant, mentioning nothing about the oversized placenta my future midwives had questioned when I had showed them my cherished pictures of Marley, lying next to his placenta in the Pyrex dish.

Again, the medical system was stripping my power and telling me what was already extremely obvious. Receiving the worthless information would have not been a problem except for the fact that baby Marley was now considered hazardous waste. The doctor's office informed me if I wanted to bury Marley I would have to pay a funeral home a minimum of $1000 for a burial.

I asked, "Well, can I just see Marley again or bury him myself?"

The doctor responded, "No, the fetus has been put into too many chemicals to be released to the public."

Fuming and tearing at the same time I questioned, "Why did the lab not have more answers?"

She replied, "The fetus was too young to do other tests."

"Why did you not tell me this before?"

The doctor said, "I did not know how old the baby had to be."

"Is this the first time you have sent a miscarried baby to the lab?"

"No." she answered indignantly.

Why did she not know this? Isn't this her job as a trained doctor who delivered babies? She did not once apologize for her mistake. I was done with unsympathetic doctors who took no responsibility for their actions.

Unfortunately, I did not choose to spend the money to bury Marley and deserted him at the laboratory to waste away while I fell deeper and deeper into the land of grief, and Dimitri continued dealing drugs and having irrational fits. What I wanted the most was to look more closely at what Dimitri and I had created and touch him, but the doctor had said I would never be allowed to touch Marley because of the chemicals that had been used in the pointless test to verify the pregnancy. I had not touched Marley before because the doctor had cautioned me that I might contaminate him and ruin the tests. Initially, I had been scared to touch him, because he looked so fragile and I thought he might fall apart if I handled him. As I said, Marley, to my surprise, was fully formed—his body was an opaque white and I could count all his fingers that had not yet separated, and

I can still vividly picture the tiny dark spots of his early-forming organs.

The name, Marley, had come to me while I had been in labor and had realized naming the baby was very important to me. Dimitri and I had talked about naming this baby Stormy because Dimitri had adored this name from the first moment he had heard it on an after-school special he had watched as a kid. He had been sleeping while I was in labor, and I had not wanted to use a name he had always wanted, especially considering the circumstances, without checking with him first. For many years, I had thought Marley was a girl, but that is another story for another book, about how I later began to suspect that Marley was a boy. Stay tuned for more about this story in my upcoming memoir, *Just A Taste*.

Academia was like comfort food so I decided to enroll in graduate school to pass the time. Since I was still stuck in my head, ignoring so much of my body and spirit, I continued to search within academia for medical answers, eventually writing my Master's thesis on the subject of HG. Slowly, I began to divorce myself from Western medicine, especially since my body had displayed such innate knowledge and strength during the labor. As I was gradually awakening spiritually, I explored the edges of alternative medicine, leading me to try acupuncture.

Before this pregnancy, I had considered having a home birth. After my body responded beautifully to birthing Marley, I knew I could birth a full-term baby at home. The doctors had shown little concern for me with HG and even messed me up more with Compazine. Little did I know how magical midwives would be. What I did know was that my body had the knowledge it needed. I am forever thankful for Marley, my first HG experience and my miscarriage for giving me the courage to give birth at home—a magnificent, empowering entrance into motherhood.

2

Midwives and More

Lost in a daze of Xanax, I felt like I could not move forward until I had a baby, eventually landing in an acupuncturist's office. He read my Chinese pulses, telling me I was too weak to carry a baby to full term. I visited him every week asking hopefully each time if my body was ready.

Finally, after a long, depressing year, he answered, "Your body is strong enough."

I rushed home to share my joy with Dimitri who exclaimed, "Here comes the baby making fluids!" as he ejaculated inside of me. Immediately I became pregnant.

Delighted and terrified I wondered if I would have HG again and/or miscarry? *How would I handle being sick, working and going to graduate school?*

I knew this would not be easy with the graduate school piece because during orientation, a professor had overheard me talking about how I had miscarried and could not wait to become pregnant again. He interrupted our conversation and told me, "You have no business being in this program if you are going to be pregnant." Our society could not even make room for pregnancy in a Master's program in Counseling Psychology that was ninety percent women.

With such a tight schedule, there was no time to gather the household supplies and resources needed for the nine months that lay ahead. Even though I longed for an HG-free pregnancy, I knew HG often repeated itself.

Throughout my packed days, I lived in fear of the potentially debilitating nausea, luckily finding a little time at work to prepare for a possible quick and long exit. I worked for a lovely, flexible woman who was completely supportive and even brought her two-year-old to the office sometimes. Work did not present the same problems to me that graduate school did.

Ironically when I succumbed to HG again, the least understanding professor was my female, family therapy professor who insisted if I did not come to the final three classes, I would have to make up the entire course because she had a strict absence policy she was unwilling to bend. Since the class was so rigidly structured that during each class we watched a specific amount of the movie, *Ordinary People*, and talked about the dysfunctional patterns among the characters, I thought it would be easy to attend the three classes the following year. She refused that idea and insisted I repeat the entire course, claiming the class discussions were especially unique to each class.

I decided to drop the class and choose my body over my mind even though that meant I would have to withdraw from the class and receive the dreaded "W" on my transcript that the perfectionistic side had never wanted. When I returned to school the following year for just that class, the professor asked the same exact questions to which the students responded practically identical answers as they had in my previous class. I was so frustrated because I believe I could have effortlessly watched the rest of the movie by myself and written a paper about the dysfunctional aspects as applied to family therapy theories, gaining more out of the paper than retaking the entire class, which was basically a slowed down version of *Ordinary People*.

This time I was glad I listened sooner to my body's cry for help—knowing to cancel my life earlier this time. I did push through a couple of days of horrible nausea before I dropped my full-time job and graduate school classes and retreated again to a dark, dark room.

A few weeks into my pregnancy, I decided to research midwifery care because I was feeling discouraged from Western medicine. I went to a few appointments and quickly realized how preposterous it was to leave the house. I stopped every two blocks, struggling each time to open the car door before I vomited, while my nausea exponentially increased with every minute I was out of bed. Eventually, I stuck to interviewing midwives who made home visits.

I ended up choosing a pair of lovely midwives who provided prenatal care at my bedside. *Genius! Why weren't more women taking advantage of home care before and up to six weeks after their babies were born?* They even drew my blood at home, sending it to the lab. This was such a gift since leaving my room exacerbated my symptoms even more.

Working with the midwives began the process of retraining my brain from the brainwashing of Western medical practitioners who had taught me to distrust my body and live a fear-based life waiting for the next medical problem to arise.

At one point, I had a new pain in my belly, and I asked the midwives what they thought it might be.

"What do you think it is?"

I started thinking to myself maybe I had made a mistake. *Why are they asking me? Aren't they trained in this?*

I answered, "I have no idea—that is why I am asking you."

They further inquired, "Does it feel like something serious?"

Now I was heavily doubting my decision. *How would I know if something was serious?*

Again I replied, "I have no idea."

They suggested there were five different possibilities of what it could be, some potentially serious, some not. They told me it was my choice whether or not to get an ultrasound. I decided to think about it and the pain went away the next day and never returned.

After a few more similar conversations, I realized they were not expecting me to defer my power to them. The midwives were curious partners who trusted my body and my instincts to grow and birth a baby naturally as women have been doing since the beginning of time. They did not play God as my previous doctors had. The midwives did not pretend to know what was wrong. They were not dismissive or all-knowing. They struck a balance working with me, not against or over me.

I felt the powerful effects of this healing approach when I finally learned and accepted this completely different method of client care. My intuition and power increased, allowing me to trust myself and my body. The midwives did not minimize me—they empowered me, shared what they knew, comforted and cared for me. It was exactly what I needed, yet so foreign to me, especially in light of having survived my childhood abuse.

Since I had shared my aspirations to eat more like the midwives, a diet consisting of whole, organic foods, I was embarrassed to admit I was craving Pop-Tarts, something I ate every morning growing up. Surprisingly, the midwives were excited I wanted to eat something, anything. They urged Dimitri to go to the store and buy me as many flavors as I wanted. This was what I needed to hear. They knew when to let go of a healthy diet, just like a parent knows those important times when to let a house rule slide. Here was another gift of HG— leading me to the midwives who could fill in for some of the balanced and safe parenting I had missed during childhood.

Another key supporter in my process was Cassandra, Dimitri's friend's sister, who had HG. Thank goodness I reached out to her— talking to her was enormously helpful and comforting. Throughout the years we talked, ending up supporting each other through many more pregnancies. The connection and information I shared with her proved highly valuable, planting the seed for my Master's thesis, which advocated for an HG support person to help navigate and alleviate HG.

Cassandra had tried hypnosis with limited success. I was still relatively new to HG and thought I might be open to this technique. My health insurance only agreed to pay if I saw the burn specialist at the local hospital to do the hypnosis. Surviving the car ride there while feeling tremendously nauseous crushed me, and once there I failed at visualizing. As an extreme doer, I could hardly sit still, let alone visualize a calm scenario. Since I was sick and stuck in my head, I was not yet receptive to this new technique.

Unable to find something that worked was extremely discouraging so I kept trying all the typical suggestions, such as sucking on lemons, ginger capsules, peppermint tea, vitamin B6 with Unisom, and acupressure bands. Still scared from the Compazine reaction, I chose to stay away from marijuana and pharmaceuticals this time. The best remedy was still to sit in a dark, dark room with absolutely no stimulation.

This pregnancy was not any better or worse than the first—I just knew what to expect. Probably due to my perfectionistic tendencies, I always felt like some kind of failure every time I would go to the emergency room for an IV so I would play games with myself and try to push myself as far as I could before receiving an IV. Even though I had learned to remove stimulation and work from my life, I had not begun to let go of these head games and ask for help when I needed it the most.

Why did I consider getting medical attention to be a failure? One reason was because I had unhealthy patterns to work out. Another issue was I hated leaving the house—it only made me feel worse, and I loathed the long, uncomfortable, unpredictable wait in the emergency room. For the most part, the nurses were accommodating and offered to set up a chair for me to receive an IV so I did not have to wait for a bed. Unfortunately, I was prone to passing out so I had to wait for a place to fully recline.

Thankfully, one day my physician friend told me not to feel guilty for getting an IV because she routinely treated college kids who showed up in the E.R. for an IV because they had a hangover. For some reason that made me feel better, convincing myself I did need to hold out until I was only vomiting bile. After each IV, my nausea subsided. I thought maybe I was on to something—some kind of solution.

However, the lack of nausea would only last until the next morning when I would wake up to the ferocious nausea. At times, I felt relieved when the nausea returned because I still worried about a miscarriage, checking my underwear for blood every time I went to the bathroom or felt a decrease in my nausea. By twenty weeks I no longer vomited several times a day—just a couple of times a week for the rest of the pregnancy. Unfortunately the constant nausea continued until the birth of my daughter.

Since the nausea was all consuming, I could hardly find ways to escape it. Sometimes I would wish to vomit more just to feel that brief reprieve from nausea that frequently follows vomiting, only to be quickly and fiercely engulfed back into the depths of the haunting nausea. After first five months of the severe, debilitating nausea, I found occasional relief when I read books—sometimes a novel a day just to keep the nausea and boredom at bay.

Mistakenly, I thought if I can read, of course, I could get out of bed. Every time I tried something like this, I had severe nausea again. By the sixth month I could handle being out of bed about two hours a week, before I would have to rest again to contain the nausea and keep food down.

Finally, I started labor at forty-one weeks, giving birth to a beautiful, calm, baby girl. Immediately, my appetite returned as the baby left my body and I was starving. Luckily, I had listened to the midwives who had suggested I ask friends to make meals to freeze ahead of time. That night I savored every bite of several servings of defrosted stuffed chicken breast.

3

Falling in Love

After my second pregnancy, I fell in love with the most rewarding career imaginable—being a stay-at-home mom. When my daughter was one year old, I had to unexpectedly return to work outside the home due to a sudden divorce. Dimitri admitted he was a heroin addict, jolting me into action. Thankfully, I came out of denial and realized I was stuck in a domestic abuse cycle, prompting me to muster the courage to end our relationship.

Although Dimitri never hit me, it was not until after my second pregnancy that I gradually woke up to the reality of my situation. Even though I had always watched the dogs cower when he would rage, I did not take action until the moment I saw the fear in my daughter's eyes during one of his intense outbursts. Holding a shaking baby in my arms was the wake-up call I needed. Sadly, I had not figured out earlier that his behavior was unacceptable and dangerous, not just to my baby, but for the dogs and me, too.

A great deal of unplanned emotional healing occurred when I divorced Dimitri. I consciously decided to be celibate for the year because I had attracted so many unsuccessful relationships in the past. I was beginning to notice how I created my own reality. If I did not take time to step back and understand how I ended up in a domestically violent relationship with a heroin addict in the first place, I feared the next relationship may be even worse than this last one. I realized the Universe and I co-created experiences for me to learn lessons. When I did not listen, the lessons would keep getting harder and harder.

A long, scary year passed filled with obtaining restraining orders, single parenting, working full-time and finishing graduate school. Then my knight in shining armor responded to my ad on Craigslist declaring, "Spiritually Grounded Single Mom Seeks Family Man." I met a wonderful man, Rob, who had been married before and in a much more abusive situation than I had been. We were ready to heal together, unaware of the long journey we had ahead of us, yet open to the healing possibilities.

When I first met Rob, I had planned to do some active healing and figure out this HG. With the highs of our new relationship, my career, and adjusting to being a stepmother to Rob's stepdaughter— who had moved in with us a few weeks before I became pregnant again—I did not find the time to do the healing I had wanted to do.

Instead of healing myself, I became ambitious as ever at work, and I was promoted six weeks after being hired. Then a year and a half later right before my third pregnancy, I was promoted again. As I was accepting the new position, I found out I was pregnant and needed to think quickly. *How would this work out if I had severe nausea and vomiting within days?*

Because the position involved the launch of a new program, I questioned if I would be able to give it the dedicated focus that start-ups needed. Even though the job was a promotion within the same company, it was part-time and a welcomed reduction in hours. Therefore, I would be receiving a decrease in pay and benefits if I accepted it and lose out if I went on some sort of leave. Fortunately, I had an extremely accommodating boss who agreed to keep me in my current position. Considering all these factors, I called the new program and rescinded my decision.

This awkward conversation happened on Friday and by Sunday, I was back to vomiting bile. I called in sick on Monday, starting my leave that lasted the entire pregnancy, receiving state and company disability the whole time. While I was pregnant, a paid parental leave policy took effect in California, and I was able to continue to receive limited pay after the baby was born. This extra money made a huge difference, allowing me to more easily transition into being a stay-at-home mom again.

Handling HG for the third time, I stuck to my formula—back to five months in a dark room, leaving only to go to the bathroom. I would go to bed at 6 p.m. because sleep was the one activity I could do splendidly during pregnancy and the only place I could find relief from the nausea. Next I would graduate to leaving my room occasionally. By the third trimester, I could spend a maximum of two hours a week out of the house, falling back in to bed for a week to recuperate.

After my first trip to the emergency room, I took Zofran,[1] which was now more widely prescribed. Since it dissolved under my tongue, Zofran was simpler to take than swallowing Compazine pills and dealing with Tigan suppositories. My body was resistant to holding on to anything, so the dissolving Zofran was absorbed too quickly for me to reject it.

Luckily, my homeopath, Carmella, had cautioned me to hold off from taking Zofran until at least ten weeks gestation when major organ formation was complete. Consuming the Zofran when I hit ten weeks helped to control the vomiting, but failed to lessen the severe nausea. I tried marijuana again—this time in tincture form and it did nothing. I could not believe I was stuck facing this awful illness and struggle again.

Not only was Carmella a homeopath, but a physician assistant who eventually wrote me prescriptions for home IVs, filled out my leave of absence paperwork, educated me about taking Zofran and introduced me to the homeopathic remedy, Sepia.

Carmella asked gently, "I know this may sound like a strange question because you are so sick, but do you have a higher sex drive?"

"Oh, my goodness, yes! I will not let my husband kiss me, but I want to have sex all the time. I have even orgasmed several times in my dreams," I proclaimed.

"Well, I am asking because the Sepia remedy treats people with HG who have an increased sex drive," she explained.

---

[1] Studies have now shown Zofran may cause birth defects.

I was so excited to hear this. Even though I did not notice an immediate change in my nausea, I was able to lower my Zofran dosage soon after taking Sepia.

Thank goodness my mom flew out from the East Coast to care for me and help around the house. I am not sure what we would have done without her. Sadly, she had to return to work after three weeks. After she left, my daughter chose to stay home from preschool most days. She loved to keep herself busy and was a joy to have around. However, without my mom, the house quickly fell apart.

When I was a single mom, my dear friend, Leslie, came over each Wednesday and kindly washed my piles of dishes. Three months into the HG, Leslie reluctantly admitted, "I am still going to come over each week, but the house is so out of control, I can't do the dishes anymore because I can't even find them."

I moaned in response, having no energy to even consider what she had said. Then during month five I came out of my dark room for the first time and clearly understood what she had said. It looked like a bomb had gone off. Rob had been understandably overwhelmed with the demands of taking care of me and the children while working full time that he had been unable to even complete basic daily tasks, such as keeping up with the laundry and dishes. Bless his heart, Rob was tremendously supportive and did the best job caring for the family and me that anyone could ever ask for.

Even though I had this incredible partner, I could not escape the nausea. Many people have experienced a bit of this intense nausea and vomiting with the stomach flu, which lasts only twenty-four hours—yet for me, the struggle lasted for months, with the constant battle of holding on for dear life. Whenever I tried to eat something, I would vomit violently. In attempt to control this, I would go as long as I could without ingesting anything—even sips of water would cause violent reactions. The memories of harsh vomiting episodes kept me away from certain foods, such as pasta and burritos, for years after being pregnant.

Another daily challenge was dry retching. Nothing would come up for hours—leaving my throat raw and my stomach muscles sore and exhausted. Trying to describe my misery reminds me there are over fifty words for "snow" in the Eskimo language because they experience it so much and can differentiate a variety of types. After vomiting so much for so long, I feel like I could create a mini dictionary of vomiting terms that only experienced vomiters would understand.

Many pregnant women, even inexperienced vomiters, can relate to foods that trigger nausea. Coffee and eggs were two foods from my childhood that would especially fuel the nausea. After a visit to my parent's house on the East Coast, Rob said he could completely understand this reaction after watching how out of control my dad became after the rush of caffeine he received from drinking coffee as he cooked eggs. My dad would make more and more critical cutting comments into the core of who I was with each cup of coffee. Every morning for eighteen years, I consciously and unconsciously experienced this emotional trauma and now the smells were triggering this memory in me. I had no idea how damaging these mornings had been to me until Rob had pointed this out.

Still wildly craving meat as I had in my last pregnancy, Rob searched for another one of my childhood favorites: prime rib. We had so much trouble locating a restaurant because of Berkeley's lack of steakhouses. We finally found a restaurant, but they did not offer carryout, only a buffet including prime rib. Weeks later, elated for the first time in months, I took my first bite of prime rib after convincing the restaurant to allow Rob to order takeout.

Food cravings continued to monopolize my thoughts, leading to our search for Italian sandwiches. We struggled to find a restaurant that started serving sandwiches before 11 a.m.—most restaurants only served sandwiches between 11 a.m. and 3 p.m. Ideally, we wanted a place where Rob could pick up a sandwich before and after work. Not until my next pregnancy did we find a restaurant that opened at 8 a.m. so I stuck to sandwiches on the weekends.

These fierce meat cravings were unknowingly leading me to one important future HG cure—massive amounts of protein. If I had just stuck with prime rib, I may have experienced less nausea and vomiting. From what I have learned about digestion, the carbohydrates from the sandwich bread were too much; they wreaked havoc on my intestines.

Lying in bed with severe stomach pain, the usual intolerable nausea and a new symptom of leg cramps, I decided to call Cassandra because talking on the phone often provided a much-needed distraction from my horrible nausea. As we were catching up, I casually mentioned I had leg cramps, and she pleaded with me to go immediately to the emergency room. She explained how this had happened to her and could be a symptom of low potassium, which could lead to a heart attack. I was extremely miserable, Rob was tremendously exhausted, and we did not want to make the effort to go to the emergency room if it was really unnecessary.

Fortunately, I ignored my hesitation to get treatment and listened to Cassandra. Blood tests confirmed I was low in potassium and dehydrated once again. I still cringe as I remember the intense pain of the potassium burning through my veins.

When I ventured out of my room during the fifth month, Rob and I considered getting married, partially because my health insurance was quite pricey. Yet we were unsure how I could even make it to the courthouse to get married. Fortunately, I started to feel a wee bit better and we quickly decided to arrange for him to take a day of work. Luckily, we succeeded on our first try and I did not even vomit the whole time I was out!

On top of the HG, our lives were a bit chaotic with blending a three-year-old and a twelve-year-old from different families. I was a bit overwhelmed learning to be a stepmother—often explaining to people that just as I was not looking for a stepdaughter, she certainly was not looking for a stepmother, but here we were quickly and intimately in each other's lives.

One place my stepdaughter and I began our connection was with knitting. I had learned to knit in my last pregnancy during my third trimester, finally feeling satisfied with being able to succeed at something. Then, in this pregnancy I taught my stepdaughter how to knit. Accomplishing something concrete helped to counteract my feelings of inadequacy and powerlessness from so many months in bed.

In addition to knitting, I frequently read a book a day, did crossword puzzles, even making them for other people. Although my mind remained active, I had to remember I could not participate in my typical activities without entering that vicious cycle of nausea and vomiting that was so hard to escape once I got myself into it. Keeping myself occupied with activities that did not make me feel worse was a meditation in itself.

Throughout my pregnancies there were definitely some angels, such as my midwives, my mom, Carmella, Leslie, Cassandra, and Rob. However, occasionally, there were people who made things worse. Some people actually dissociated when I asked them to do simple tasks, such as emptying the trash. One time a mom offered to come over and clean and brought her child to play with mine. She sat in my room, stimulating me with her drama-filled life, exacerbating my nausea. I needed to shift the focus and direct her to help as she had initially offered. I kindly asked her to take out the trash. She ignored my request, looking off into the distance. She continued on about herself, and I gently mentioned it again explaining how sick I was and how much it would help if she emptied the trash. Again, no response. She ended up leaving when my daughter burst into tears after her son called my daughter "stupid." Now I was worse off, with increased nausea and left with a crying child.[2]

The years of the HG pregnancies were an opportunity for me to see other people's character more clearly. I could no longer endure relationships with people or situations that were damaging to me. Without HG, I would have still kept these people in my life who I have watched go on to destroy other people's lives.

During month seven, I became even sicker with pneumonia and my first-ever sinus infection. I remember sitting all day and night upright in a chair struggling to breathe and deathly exhausted from

---

[2] For those of you familiar with my book, *Understanding Your Child as a Spiritual Gift*, I cannot help but apply that channeling theory here. Her son had hit my daughter because the mother had wanted to hit me for asking her to help. My daughter had started crying so much and would not stop because she was "channeling" how upset I was that I was worse off now.

the HG and pneumonia, questioning how I would survive—*Will I even get a next breath?*

Gradually, I healed from the pneumonia. Two months later I birthed Arcata, who surprisingly weighed 9 ½ pounds, and instantly I felt like eating again. We pulled stuffed chicken breast out of the freezer and I feasted again, my body strangely capable of immediately and easily digesting everything without a problem now that I was no longer pregnant.

Arcata's baby years were another powerful spiritual journey for our family, which is discussed in depth in my book, *Understanding Your Child as a Spiritual Gift*. She rocked our world uncontrollably for two and a half years, crying non-stop until we realized she was expressing my husband's unexpressed feelings. He had been an extreme people pleaser for over forty years and all his unexpressed feelings were coming through her. Now that we have figured out their connection, she is the most cheerful and light-hearted child.

Looking back, I am so thankful to the HG for knocking me down again so I had no other choice than to place my career on hold for the entire pregnancy. After my paid leave ended, I could not imagine returning to work, which had lost so much meaning compared to the joy of being a stay-at-home mom. Even if I had wanted to work, Arcata was one of those incredibly clingy babies who cried incessantly. I had watched friends of mine with babies like this who were asked to leave daycare after daycare.

Through applying this new parenting theory to my life, I have learned how much our children's behaviors are windows into our souls. This book is another platform that examines how our children come here to teach us where and how we need to grow.

4

Almost There

Exhausted from raising my stepdaughter, three-year-old and extremely clingy, demanding, sleepless baby while recovering from HG, I lacked sufficient time and energy for reflection and healing. I researched what little information had surfaced since my thesis, throwing together a haphazard plan of what healing protocols I wanted to try before I became pregnant again.

Two particular healing techniques stood out: a liver cleanse using the Polarity diet and removing my mercury fillings. However, I had to stop nursing before I could safely do either of these, which was particularly challenging because my children and I were unwilling to give up the sweet bonding of tandem nursing. As the baby grew into a toddler, she gnawed my nipples raw every time she nursed, leaving me with bleeding nipples that refused to heal. This pain motivated me to wean my children.

After I stopped nursing, I researched the complicated process of mercury filling removal, learning that when a person is allergic to mercury the potential for problems is high. Overwhelmed with all the information, I was unsure how to figure out if I was allergic to mercury, so I decided to take the usual precautions like using a dental dam, and chose to forgo the extremely disruptive protocol of taking detoxing pills every two hours throughout the night. Lucky for me, I was not allergic to mercury so the procedure and aftermath went smoothly. At first, I did not think it made a significant difference in my healing, however, we have since learned that my husband and his family are particularly allergic to mercury. Perhaps, removing the mercury benefited the next two babies as they were developing in utero.

The Polarity diet, which consists of a spicy oily morning beverage and unlimited fresh fruit and vegetables, helped cleanse my liver. In Chinese medicine, the liver is known for storing the emotion of anger, which had accumulated in response to my childhood abuse. Physically cleansing this organ was a necessary step in preparing my body to release the emotions I had been holding in there for years.

Revamping my nutrition was next on my list. Since money was a consideration, I went to a nutritionist paid for by my health insurance, giving Western medicine another chance. For my appointment, we met in her office that was lined with boxes of packaged foods. I knew I had made a mistake. Processed food was not going to repair my digestion. She had hardly heard of HG, admitting there was not much she could tell me I did not already know. I knew I must continue my journey without the medical establishment and figure out the answers on my own.

First, I tried to cut out packaged foods, going back and forth with an all or none approach, beating myself up when I did not shun all processed foods. Next, I avoided bringing the processed foods into the house. If I chose to eat packaged foods outside of the house, I could forgive myself and just slowly wean myself by controlling what I ate in the house. Then I experimented with giving up sugar, applying these same house rules to my sugar consumption.

The single most important dietary change I have ever made was giving up NutraSweet. When I was addicted to Diet Coke, I did not ever think I could live without it. Because I could not go a day without at least one Diet Coke, I thought this would be a huge challenge; however, it was the easiest dietary change I have ever made and the most significant change I have made for my health, especially my mental health[3].

---

[3] Here is scientific support http://bit.ly/2foFIAG to what I have long intuitively known—how destructive NutraSweet is.

During this year, I also got tested for Helicobacter Pylori, an intestinal bacteria, which is found in many people with HG. The result was negative. I felt let down, yet again, when a possible cure for my HG evaporated.

Piece by piece, I was learning the best way to tackle HG was to revisit techniques that had been unsuccessful in the past. I gave hypnotherapy another chance—this time focusing on past childhood abuse. I was more open to it this time, but still had trouble completely letting go. The therapist asked me to listen to tapes at home that she had created from our sessions. As an extreme doer, completing the assigned task was not difficult, but actually letting go and relaxing were the challenging parts for me. Hypnotherapy proved more effective in between pregnancies because of how much HG hijacked my motivation during each pregnancy.

In the midst of all these healing attempts, our stepdaughter, Samantha, left quickly and somewhat unexpectedly under particularly dramatic circumstances. To be blunt, Rob's ex-wife makes Dimitri look like an angel. His ex-wife dropped off Samantha on our doorstep so she could escape to the Caribbean, chasing a married man she had met on the Internet while simultaneously initiating court proceedings in the U.S. to strip Rob of his parental rights to Samantha, who he had been raising since she was one month old.

Although watching Samantha leave is one of the biggest regrets I have ever had, I am not sure if holding on would have made any difference. As I have said before, I had to let the drama out of my life if I wanted to heal. Sometimes this required releasing an important person who had been innocently tangled in the mess. When the person is as special as Samantha, reunification happens at just the right time—and in this case, she surprised us on Thanksgiving about two years after she had abruptly left.

Another person I am waiting to have back in my life is Cassandra. Unfortunately, we lost touch during this pregnancy because her number no longer worked one day when I called. Cassandra had been facing an unbelievably difficult dilemma in the face of her HG. She had survived two extremely challenging HG pregnancies with her new husband. Her oldest daughter from a previous marriage had been diagnosed with a life-threatening illness. The only possible cure was a stem cell transplant from a full biological sibling, which her daughter did not have. Cassandra acted quickly and talked with her ex-husband, and they decided he would donate his sperm for another pregnancy. Her current husband said he refused to support Cassandra through another HG pregnancy. Her husband threatened, "If you do this, I will leave you." She chose to try to save her daughter and became a single mom with HG. And that is when we lost touch.

What an awful decision to face. HG is difficult enough without having to make such choices. Of course, I cannot help but label her husband as a jerk—but then again I have lived through HG enough times to know it takes an incredibly special partner to stand by watching and supporting someone struggling with HG.

Preparing for another HG pregnancy, I had time to put my affairs when I learned I was pregnant again. I gathered paper towels, plates, and cups, letting go of my environmental friendly decision to forbid the use of these products in the house. Since I had only a week, ten days at most, before I was violently nauseous, I quickly stocked up on other household supplies, did some extra cleaning, paid outstanding bills and alerted my supporters.

Rob had exhausted his sick leave during my last HG pregnancy and the paternity leave that followed. Thankfully, my mom still had vacation time from work, coming again for three weeks to help after my first IV. She traveled across the country when the nausea was at its peak and kept planning to leave, but I was not getting better— only worse. I cannot imagine what it was like for her to see her grown-up baby so ill.

Days after my mother left, Rob went to the doctor because he had been pushing in his abdominal hernia for over a year, never letting anyone know about it. The doctors urged him to have immediate surgery. We called my mom and bless her heart she returned the next day, and Rob had the surgery that week. He fretted over his nausea from the Vicodin, moaning and whining how sick he felt and how he could not handle it.

Until then, I do not think Rob had registered how much I had been suffering. Although he had been incredibly supportive during these HG pregnancies, I was unable to muster any sympathy for his temporary nausea. That night Rob quickly fell asleep and in the morning his nausea was only a faint memory while my nausea continued to haunt me.

In the middle of all this, I decided to try something I had been unwilling to do because of the extra expense—a home IV. Back then, there was an initial set-up fee of $300 with each visit costing $150. Since I mostly controlled my HG in a dark room with a complete absence of stimulation, I only required a few IV treatments each pregnancy. Four home IV fluid treatments cost under $1000—much less than the cost of one emergency room visit. Although the insurance company paid for the hospital fees, the costs added up quickly with a $100 copay each visit. The extra money for someone to come to my house was worth it because I could remain in bed and keep a line in without getting pricked over and over.

Coincidentally, the home health nurse assigned to me turned out to be a neighbor. He was a lovely man who became a friendly face in the neighborhood. Instead of meeting destructive people, I was cutting ties with difficult people as I was shedding those parts of myself, making room for the kind souls out there.

During my daughter's third birthday party, I could only come out of my room for about two minutes before quickly retreating. The noise was so overwhelming, fueling my nausea. I knew to be very careful because once the nausea reached a certain point it was impossible to shake—increasing every moment making it difficult to eat or drink anything and before I knew it I would be dehydrated again, which would make me even more nauseous. I had designed my life around avoiding this vicious cycle which often jumpstarted uncontrollable vomiting. Fortunately, after resting for an hour, I came out for the cake and candles.

After my mom left, the kids no longer had a constant distraction so we let them watch movies. We had never owned a television and normally the children were only allowed to watch movies one night a week. After watching movies every day for a week, reaching thirteen hours of movies in one day, my daughter told me she did not think unlimited movies were a good idea, and she suggested we impose some media limits. The next day she chose playing with toys all day instead of watching movies. I thought she might begin to self-regulate, but she still needed reminders to turn it off because media can be so addicting.

Many people urged me to put my kids in school, instead of homeschooling, arguing how much easier it would be for me. I do not subscribe to our society's disregard for children and the constant push to hide children away somewhere. Their squeals and delights in the simple things were what got me through such trying times growing their siblings. I worked hard from bed to make sure they were occupied with play dates both at my house and outside the house. I still smile when I see the three-year-old handprints on my laundry room wall from the day my daughter and her friend discovered the paints.

Children also love to help and mine were eager to fetch me a tissue or grab a snack that I was craving. Bystanders also failed to realize the restrictiveness of school schedules. I cannot imagine how much harder this HG would have been with trying to get homework done, struggling to wake the kids up in the morning and rushing around picking them up and dropping them off. Life at home provided a more natural rhythm and since I was going to bed at 6 p.m., I would have barely seen them if they had been in school.

Using walkie-talkies never occurred to me so I just relied on yelling a reminder to watch less movies from my bed when I could muster enough energy. I am amazed at how much parenting can be done from bed: limiting media, scheduling play dates, coordinating activities and on a good day doing a short, quiet activity with one of them while in remaining bed (refer to Appendix A: *52 Ideas for Pregnancy Sickness, Bedrest, and the Newborn Weeks*).

This fourth time around I repeated the Zofran protocol, holding off until the tenth week of pregnancy. In light of recent research highlighting the possible dangers of Zofran in the first trimester, I am glad I waited to use it even though week seven through nine were so powerfully disarming—preferring instead to rely on IVs and a dark room to keep me afloat.

Cravings still permeated my consciousness, but unfortunately the restaurant with prime rib stopped serving it. Continuing his rock star role as ultimate caretaker and breadwinner, Rob made prime rib at home. I continued to obsess about Italian sandwiches—grateful we had finally found a restaurant that served sandwiches for breakfast.

When I was fifteen weeks pregnant and still miserably nauseous, a marvelous opportunity arose for me to attend an energetic training. Rob had been treating me with this energy work that was similar to Reiki, a successful tool for reducing nausea in patients with cancer. The energy class usually took place in a conference room, but this time the training had low enrollment so someone offered their house for the training. I explained my situation to the teacher who described the layout of the house: a room with a bed faced the doorway to the living room where the class would be taught. This sounded perfect! I dragged myself there every day while my mother took care of everything at the house.

It was unbelievable how the pieces fit so well together—my mom had just returned to help Rob recover from hernia surgery, and there was a training in a house with a bed for me! This energy training did not immediately make a large difference, but over time helped clear unseen obstacles, making me ready to let go of HG in my final pregnancy.

Just like my previous pregnancies, every time the baby was born, I immediately felt like eating after the baby left my body—gobbling up that stuffed chicken breast again. This time my anxiety was extremely high, and I relied on taking my encapsulated placenta to balance my hormones and quell my fears of another baby. Preparing the placenta as medicine was another trick the midwives shared with me (refer to Appendix B: *The Magic of Midwives* for more midwifery tricks).

Surprisingly, I was the most nervous to be a mom this time around. In retrospect, I see how my third daughter came to teach me how to relax and have fun. This lesson increased my post-partum anxiety, which I believe, represented my resistance to this tall order.

5

HG Free at Last

In my last pregnancy I finally escaped HG. I was so blessed to have my dream husband, Rob, perform acupuncture on me every other day—a crucial treatment that controlled my first trimester nausea and vomiting. Rob is a remarkable man and father who taught himself acupuncture during each newborn phase, holding each baby in the sling, always taking the first shift late into the night while studying large acupuncture meridian charts he had purchased for our walls.

Besides Rob's acquisition of acupuncture skills, we relied on the acupuncture points discussed in *Managing Morning Sickness* by Miriam Erick. The author included a study from Exeter, England where fifty-five women with pregnancy sickness between six and ten weeks gestation were divided into three groups depending on their HG symptoms. Each group received fifteen-minute treatments, either by inserting a needle or by holding a toothpick on the point. The first group used the points: Conception Vessel 12, Pericardium 6, Spleen 4, and Stomach 36. Mothers in this group mainly complained of nausea, lack of motivation, stuffiness in the chest, and a moist tongue.

The second group was treated with points: Conception Vessel 12, Pericardium 6, and Stomach 44. The primary symptoms of this group were nausea and vomiting right after eating, heartburn, metal and sour tastes, burning stomach pain, and constipation. The last group experienced vivid dreams, nausea, insomnia, dark urine, bitter tastes and abdominal pain and tried points: Conception Vessel 12, Pericardium 6, and Stomach 34. All three groups experienced a reduction in their nausea, even when toothpicks were used instead of the needles. Researchers thought that the reduction in symptoms occurred because of stimulation of the A-delta nerve fibers in the skin and muscles.

Rob treated me with a combination of these points every other day since I related to many of these symptoms such as constipation, vivid dreams, nausea and vomiting right after eating, severe abdominal pain, unpleasant tastes in my mouth, dark urine and a moist tongue, which presented itself as voluminous saliva in my situation. After my thesis research revealed few successful treatments, I was extremely excited there were acupuncture points for these specific symptoms. The points overlapped among the groups so my final protocol looked like this: Conception Vessel 12, Pericardium 6, Spleen 4, Stomach 33, Stomach 36, and Stomach 44 (refer to pp. 61-63, 98 for "how to" information).

When acupuncture needles were not available, I used acupressure, which involves applying slight pressure to a specified point. One extremely useful point was the Triple Warmer point, which is located four fingers width from the wrist crease on the outer arm. It is directly opposite the typical nausea point Pericardium 6, which is located four finger widths up from the inner wrist crease.

On alternate days, Rob treated me with cranial sacral massage, which involves gentle manipulation of the bones of the skull. In between pregnancies I visited a cranial sacral practitioner with Rob. She showed him a few tips and offered to teach him as much as he wanted to know.

Rob and I have been blessed with a variety of healers wanting to share their methods with us. A majority of alternative healers tend to want people to heal themselves and seem less interested in making a profit from someone's misery. Since these health care providers have a wealth of information to share, I highly recommend taking someone with you to the appointment with a pen and paper in hand to take notes.

In addition to the acupuncture and cranial sacral, I relied heavily on the Korean remedy of barley tea for the nausea. I could actually leave the house during the first trimester as long as I had barley tea with me, taking sips throughout my day. I moved more slowly than usual, but other than that I could handle the nausea and occasional vomiting.

Medical marijuana was finally effective this pregnancy. After taking a tincture specifically designed for nausea, I still felt nauseous, but I did not seem to care or attach to the idea. It was as though the marijuana let me stand outside of myself away from the nausea. This allowed me to toss aside the nausea instead of grasping it as my new identity.

For the first time, I decided to hire help before I got pregnant since there were three kids now. When hiring our babysitter, we told her we expected her to entertain the three kids as well as clean the house and take care of me. She was skilled at completing household tasks while providing activities to keep the children satisfied; I was ecstatic I had found someone to replace me. This time I did not require as much assistance, but the kids and house still needed a lot of care.

Taking Floradix, a liquid herbal iron supplement, was a regular part of my previous pregnancies because my blood work always revealed I was low in iron. This time my body was willing to ingest almost anything, except the Floradix, so my husband starting making beet kvass, a fermented drink, to nourish me.

My day started with huge amounts of protein only, consuming about three hot dogs and three hamburgers for breakfast alone. After the first trimester, I could eat whatever I wanted and craved Indian food. This time I did not have to search for it or freak out when it was not available.

In past pregnancies, I had difficulty finding treatments that worked, often feeling so miserable it was impossible to be motivated to do a treatment if I did not see immediate results. Often it was unclear if a technique had made a difference. What finally healed me was my ability to mix and match techniques while learning not to be attached to one specific outcome, nudging me to be less absolute and more willing to accept treatments that had not worked in previous pregnancies. Ironically, I was more flexible in some areas, such as trying a healing technique. Though in other areas of my life, I had actually become more uptight in response to developing healthy boundaries and learning to have strict boundaries with the people I let into my life.

I know this all sounds like a lot of work. However, HG management takes an unbelievable effort—much more than the measly thirty to sixty minutes for these interventions. The added benefit was I could do activities outside the house and exit without vomiting gear—such as plastic bags and a change of clothes. The cranial massage and acupuncture only took fifteen to thirty minutes a day. Making the tea was easy and taking a dropperful of medical marijuana was effortless. Staying away from carbohydrates was not too hard because of how much better I felt without them. In the moment of choice, a good tasting cookie versus days in bed made staying away from temptation more manageable.

When I woke up one morning during the thirteenth week of pregnancy, the nausea and vomiting had disappeared. I had been waiting for a normal trimester for so long, and I could not believe the relaxing second trimester I had heard so much about was here! I would no longer have to miss so many milestones, such as weddings and birthday parties, as I had been doing for the past ten years. I actually hiked for five miles one day. This may not seem like much, but after being unable to barely walk without feeling extremely nauseous and entering some vicious cycle of vomiting, this was an enormous feat.

Enjoying my second trimester so much, I was taken aback as I entered my third trimester the week after my five-mile hike—I fell to the floor in agonizing pain. My pubic bone had split. I am unsure if it was the hike or something else that caused the splitting of my pubic bone. Upon reflection, I can see how this experience connected to my healing from past sexual violation. At the time, I did not know what to do. HG was bad, but I could still go to the bathroom on my own. With this, I could not move.

I notified the midwives immediately and of course they were again prepared to help—arriving within the hour to put in back into place. I stayed on the floor perfectly still for that hour. One small movement resulted in excruciating pain. My wonder at the skill of the midwives continued as they reset my pubic bone and even taught Rob how to do it, anticipating a reoccurrence.

My pubic bone separated a few more times during the pregnancy and was equally frightening each time because I had to wait until the midwives or my husband were available. I stayed in constant contact with my husband so he could rescue me when needed. This was difficult, but well worth it compared to women who have been ordered to remain on bed rest because of this immobilizing condition.

Below is a section from my book, *Understanding Your Child as a Spiritual Gift*, which explains how I realized this pregnancy was a gift, helping me finally resolve issues central to my HG.

My pregnancy with Jackson and his birth were filled with so much healing and hope. One week before my husband's scheduled vasectomy, Rob had a dream in which a little girl held his hand and said, "Will you be my daddy?" He had shared two similar dreams with me, and on both occasions, I became pregnant shortly after. I was unhappy he was having a vasectomy and definitely did not feel done having children. The day before his vasectomy, he decided to cancel it because he had kept thinking about the girl in the dream and felt he was denying this spirit if he did not let her come through us.

Pregnant six weeks later, I was shocked, delighted and scared because my pregnancies were so difficult. We both wanted another girl. The girl in the dream had said her name was June. My due date was the end of May, and I had previously had each of my three girls later than the due date so we thought her message was that she would be born in June. Then at thirty-five weeks, I had an ultrasound that showed I was having a boy. Rob immediately started crying. I was disappointed but felt unattached. Jackson, who normally had been quite active in the womb, did not move inside me for the next 24 hours. He sensed our sadness.

We were scared to have a boy. We had our superficial reasons for not wanting a boy, such as boys are rough, boys are too hyper, and we already know how to raise girls. We did not know there were spiritual reasons that would be revealed once we were learned we were having a boy.

Within 24 hours I realized why I had never wanted to have a boy. I had long known I had been sexually abused, but I thought I had done enough work in this life to avoid addressing the issue any further. However, with the news of a son, I knew this was not the case. I began to reject my plans to nurse him and could not imagine changing his diapers. This was so surprising because I had nursed one of my children until she was 5 years old. I called the midwives, and they said they expected such a reaction from me, explaining how this was a common experience for women who have been sexually abused. The midwives referred me to a therapist who specialized in this area. I underwent four sessions, including Eye Movement Desensitization and Reprocessing (EMDR), to clear my body and mind of the sexual abuse trauma. When Jackson was born, I was able to nurse him, but was still leery of changing his diapers. I worked through it and am now delighted to have a son and aware that my healing from sexual abuse is not yet complete.

The above excerpt illustrates some of the emotional healing that occurred during this pregnancy, coinciding with the long-awaited healing from HG. As I write this, it occurs to me that healing from HG was part of what I was waiting for before I could feel done having kids—the other part was having a boy. I still have more work ahead of me on my journey in this life, but I am thankful to the HG and my children for showing me some of the missing pieces of the puzzle.

In the following chapters, I will switch gears and examine perfectionism more closely, elaborate on adversity as a gift, summarize alternative healing techniques and provide further resources in the Appendices.

6

Letting Go of Perfectionism

This chapter explores perfectionism: defining it, discussing how it develops, providing stories about how it related to my HG, and sharing useful tips for lessening perfectionism, interwoven with anecdotes of my experience as a perfectionist.

Perfectionism is a powerful drive to control yourself and others in order to cover up doubt, judgment, shame and vulnerability, leading to disrupted relationships with yourself and others, and even contributing to physical problems. Researchers agree perfectionism is destructive, even though it is often erroneously a highly regarded trait, especially in our American culture. Elizabeth Gilbert comments how perfectionism "disguises itself as a virtue."

The root of perfectionism is fear, rearing its ugly head in a variety of ways. I used to think of it as just an obsession about how things physically looked—never quite able to personally jump on the appearance bandwagon. For me, perfectionism erupts mostly when efficiency and planning are at stake or when attempting to control what other people say or do. Then there is the perfectionistic self-talk that eats my inner core while the outside world remains unaware of my internal dialogue. For most of my life, I have listened to my inner dialogue, failing to realize most people do not habitually disempower themselves like this.

Often before getting out of the bed in the morning, I challenge myself to refrain from criticizing anyone in my family. Often within minutes of walking out of my room, I see or hear something that awakens an almost uncontrollable urge to criticize. *How do I let the clothes I just picked up last night remain on the floor? Do I ignore, yet again, another sugar-infused breakfast Rob and I have repeatedly agreed is an unhealthy way to start the day?*

This is when I ask myself to focus on what I am grateful for. *What is something positive I can say? If I believe I create my own reality, how can I practice that now? Can I ignore what is frustrating me?* I push myself to say, "Thank you for making breakfast," instead of focusing on a litany of other complaints, which would only bring more and more problems into my awareness with every criticism.

When I look at my worst parenting moments, perfectionism is often the underlying issue that draws out the negative aspects of my parenting. *How many times have I yelled at my kids because I am trying to make something perfect? Has it ever been worth it?* No, they just end up feeling bad about themselves.

My friend told me a story, which has always stuck with me, about the importance of catching yourself before you speak and act. She admitted how terribly she had felt after she had watched a video of herself from her son's birthday party. Because of this, she advises parents to imagine what it would be like to watch a video of yourself yelling at your kid, keeping that image in your head to prevent yourself from taking your stress out on them. Big events, like birthday parties, are what a child frequently remembers and are often stressful days filled with unrealistic expectations, enticing us to lose sight of enjoying the moment.

Birthday parties were some of my most challenging perfectionistic moments. Because I was obsessed with planning while trying to stick to a tight budget, I would constantly snap at Rob for weeks before and all during the party. What a relief when I finally began to trust Rob could handle these events without my intense preparation. Wrapped in my fear, I forgot Rob was a teacher, more than capable of handling a room full of children. When I started to prepare less and let him just wing it, the parties were much more enjoyable for everyone.

Just after I moved from the East Coast to the West Coast, I began my struggle with HG and my initial recovery from perfectionism. The first of many tests preparing me to let go of my perfectionism occurred the first month I was here—I noticed typos on the front page of the San Francisco Chronicle! Beside myself, my perfectionistic inspired judgment exploded into full force mode. As it took hold, some part of me thought I was better than the staff of the newspaper. How silly is that? Some wounded part of me wanted to think and feel superior to some strangers at the newspaper.

Reflecting upon my egotistical judgment, I can hardly believe how much my judgments have polluted this planet by trying to cover up my insecurities. As a recovering perfectionist, I can now imagine that maybe the staff left the office early to see a child's performance, do some much-needed self-care, such as getting a massage, or maybe indulge in something fun, such as going to laughter yoga. Whatever the reason, more time and energy was not wasted on trying to find every single error. In Japanese art, the artist purposely leaves a flaw in their work. What flaws are we covering up in ourselves when we judge others for making a mistake?

One mantra to counteract this counterproductive coping strategy of perfectionism is "Breathe In Blessing, Breathe Out Judgment." Whenever I have a negative thought about someone else, I repeat this mantra. The blessing is for the person I am being negative toward and the hurting part of myself that needs healing, as a result of my emotionally hollow upbringing.

Another experience that challenged my perfectionistic core also unfolded during that first month in California—attending Chi Gong class. The teacher enthusiastically promoted Chi Gong, emphasizing the importance of daily practice, convincing my searching soul this was the discipline for me. I focused intensely, trying to remember the exact poses for the entire sequence by the end of the initial class, asking lots of questions about how to do it exactly right. At the end of class, the teacher approached me, sharing she had no concerns about me actually doing the exercises at home—but a concern about when will I learn how to just "be?"

This reminded me of how I used to fume at my ex-boyfriend, perplexed and baffled by his inertia. He would just sit on the couch doing nothing—he mentioned something about "relaxing," which was a foreign concept to me. Unable to tolerate relaxation for anyone, I would condemn him, arguing that he was just staring at a blank wall wasting his time.

My lack of understanding should not come as a surprise because my dad used to wake me up on weekend mornings at 7 a.m. for no reason. When asked why he did this, he would claim there was stuff to do. However, this was his delusion—we had no need for early rising, such as living on a farm, and I was a straight A student with two jobs. As I started to heal, I slowly realized I had learned from my dad how to constantly do but never how to truly relax—only toying with the idea of "being instead of doing" without ever fully embracing it. When I came head to head with HG I had to stop my life and let go of another layer of this early dysfunctional pattern. The message from HG was loud and clear—now was the time to learn how to just "be."

Seventeen years later, after my first brush with HG, I still struggle with just being. Leaving my career behind was a tremendous help, but now as I birth myself as a writer, I have to be careful not to fall back into my old patterns. After writing more than half of this book from stories that were inside of me, I tried to find my HG journals and realized I had recently gotten rid of them, inspired by *The Life-Changing Magic of Tidying Up* by Marie Kondo. She suggests only keeping what brings you joy. The journals were filled with some dark times and were mainly a concrete collection of times, diets and treatments in a long, boring format. With the disposal of my HG journals went some of the remnants of my lingering perfectionism. I realized I could use the writing of this book as another challenge to examine my perfectionism. My adoring husband also assured me I did not need the journals because the experience was still inside of me.

Until I started writing, I had no idea how much the story was begging to come out—over one thousand words a day poured out of me after reading *Big Magic* by Elizabeth Gilbert. This burst of writing surprised me because the month was particularly busy with an exhausting collection of kid activities mixed with the added commitments of the Jewish High Holidays. When I read Gilbert's theory that ideas magically travel around looking for someone willing to share the idea with the world, I instantly knew this was what had been happening to me with my HG story, and I felt compelled to share it with others. Unfortunately, Gilbert explains how people are usually distracted and do not hear the calling, and those who do hear it often ignore the voice so the idea moves on to someone else. Gilbert further explains this is why people often accuse others of writing the book they were planning to write. With this new perspective, I felt so much more alive, truly creating from a place of inner inspiration and meaning compared to how I had been robotically doing things because I thought I "should"—solely operating from some ill-conceived notions of perfectionism and judgment.

Before reading Gilbert's book, every time I considered writing a book about HG, I rejected the thought because it seemed so exhausting. Now I feel encouraged to write this book instead of looking at it as another task to trudge through—no longer struggling to unleash my creativity from a place of burden. Because of her book, I kept thinking how much this book had tried to come through me and how energy flooded me when people talked about pregnancy sickness. I had already lived the toughest part of writing this book: the actual living with HG in four pregnancies on and off for ten years—*why not complete this journey once and for all?*

Somehow I have held on to the research papers from my thesis, reminding me I still have a little more to let go from the intellectual, perfectionistic parts of myself. I found the old research papers as I was searching for my lost HG journals. I wanted to throw the articles away but could not bring myself to do it. I skimmed them, refreshing myself about how baffling and debilitating HG is, able to part with only half of them. I took notes from the rest and will hold on to them until I publish this book. Hopefully, by then, I will be trusting enough to dispose of them.

That last collection of sentences is one of the first paragraphs I wrote for this book and now I am doubting I will even use much, if any, of the research papers. Part of me wants to lament the lost time of re-reading well over fifty journal articles. The other recovering side of me realizes how the re-reading was part of the process—even if I do not use any of it. This brings us to the old adage of "life is a journey." I am learning to embrace the journey without being fixated on always having to "do"—realizing I do not always have to focus on winning a "game." HG was an arduous journey overflowing with healing opportunities that continue to unfold even as I write this book.

This game playing and always thinking I am trying to win something brings out my competitiveness, causing me to doubt my HG experience warranted a book because there are many more severe cases. My perfectionistic, competitive side engulfs me, tempting me to believe an experience does not count unless you endure the worst-case scenario. I am so thankful to be on the path of discarding that useless belief.

Another trap of perfectionism is all-or-nothing thinking. Perfectionists often excel in areas where they can appear perfect and avoid areas that require their weaknesses to be exposed. This type of thinking affects me the most in terms of housecleaning. On the rare occasions I do clean the house, I am so stressed afterward trying to keep it the way I cleaned it. Since I am not very visual or concerned about presentation as much as efficiency, most of the time I let the house slide to the nothing side of the continuum, often reasoning— *why even bother cleaning when it will be messed up so quickly?*

Black-or-white thinking also came into play with my HG. I vacillated between extreme states of being incredibly demanding and incredibly self-reliant—like many other perfectionists. Frequently, I would panic, yelling for someone to drop everything in order to shut the curtains when I saw a sliver of light peaking through or to fetch food when I had a craving. Other times I would lay there wasting away, losing weight and failing to ask for the IV I sorely needed. Learning to balance these extremes was another HG lesson for me.

Besides competitiveness and all-or-nothing thinking, perfectionism leads to self-doubt. When I wrote the preface and first chapter, I felt so excited and showed it to a few early readers who shared my enthusiasm. Then I started to worry. The early readers commented how captivated they were with the story in the first chapter, wondering what Dimitri would do next. I mentioned to my husband my fear that the chapters of the pregnancies with him would be so less engaging because our lives are healthier, worrying again to myself, *do I have enough for the book?*

I had planned to give each pregnancy a chapter. *Will that still work?* I knew I still had another pregnancy with Dimitri to write about, but I felt discouraged and questioned myself, *What if I did not have enough for the other chapters?* Fed up with this nasty side of perfectionism that causes me to doubt myself and my creativity, I coached myself, shushing my inner doubt, convincing myself what I needed would come to me. *I must move forward and not let the perfectionism get the better of me.* I had to quiet the destructive voice inside my head and just keep writing. As you read in the previous chapters, it turns out I had more than enough stories. Using the mantra, "Breathe In Faith, Breathe Out Doubt," helped propel me forward and silence my unsupportive chatter.

This mantra also heals the thoughts of doubt that come from being so hard on yourself as a perfectionist—a trap many of us easily fall into. This intense pushing of myself for numerous years is one of the primary reasons I was challenged with HG, and learning to let go of my perfectionism helped to release some of my severe nausea and vomiting.

Several authors talk about perfectionism, offering their thoughts and inspiration. The American writer Rebecca Solnit points out, "So many of us believe in perfection, which ruins everything else, because the perfect is not only the enemy of the good; it's also the enemy of the realistic, the possible and the fun." Healing requires me to look for more ways to have fun and less ways to seek approval from external means. A friend recently posted on Facebook that she had won the Laughter Award at work so I congratulated her, commenting that I was striving for more fun in my life and wanted to win that kind of award.

Gilbert suggests you keep your mind busy when she says, "give your mind a job to do, or else it will find a job to do, and you might not like the job it invents." She continues that your mind without a job is like an unworked border collie; it will destroy the house unless you give it jobs to do. I even believe if the mind does not have the right job, it will begin to destroy your body. HG was my wake-up call to not only change my environment and leave my domestically violent relationship, but also to change the deep-seated thoughts and beliefs that led me to the relationship in the first place.

There are different ways to give the mind a job. Physical exercise, mantras and creative projects are positive activities to keep the mind busy. Be careful with social media and television, potentially destructive employers of the mind, which can easily become addicting like drugs and zap your energy, wreaking havoc on your system, feeding your mind with gossip to fuel the judgment of yourself and others.

Giving up the news is another powerful healing tool. Andrew Weil, author of *8 Weeks to Optimum Health*, advocates doing a news fast. Try for a day and then a week. In this day and age, it is virtually impossible to shun all news, so try this game. When you hear a news story, challenge yourself to refrain from asking questions or becoming engaged in the story. The more you think and talk about the story, the more you invite drama into your life, perpetuating judgment and fear in you.

Gilbert also advises "done is better than good." For perfectionists, this is a valuable mindset. Some healers of perfectionism advocate for people to strive to do their best, but I think this is difficult for a perfectionist to figure out because they are often so consumed with controlling their emotions, paddling upstream while fearing for their life. Perfectionism drives a person to struggle against the river of life instead of accessing the flow that is readily available. When I merge into that flow relaxing down the river, I can more easily throw away doubt and judgment, replacing those reactions with a response—starting with calm, centered self-talk and a worldview that emphasizes faith and blessing.

When my chronic pain starts to flare, I interpret it as my body screaming out, as it did with HG, letting me know I am pushing against the river, falling back into my old, destructive patterns of perfectionism. As I release more and more unhealthy beliefs, my body feels better and better. However, chronic pain is a life-long struggle for me and I still suffer at times from unexplained pain that moves around my body—a cue for me to switch gears and acknowledge my feelings instead of burying them in my body.

Unless I enter the flow, my mind tries to paddle against the current, up the river, and in the wrong direction, engulfing me with feelings of being overwhelmed and out of control, which are similar to the feelings I suppressed while being abused as a child. I believe I will keep experiencing these disorienting feelings until I fully change my belief system and realize now I am safe to inhabit my body and flow down the river with the current—no longer needing to struggle upstream and fight against it.

Brené Brown, author of *The Gifts of Imperfection*, notices how non-perfectionistic people in her research seem to be "slow to judge themselves and others," most likely because they are able to access their flow more readily. When I am in my flow, I have no time or desire to judge others and make it perfect. The moment I start to want perfection, I know I am beginning to turn in the opposite direction—a recipe that only adds struggle to my life, not ease.

As I discuss the effect of trauma on perfectionism, I want to mention a new paradigm called adverse childhood experiences (ACE), which is defined as "a traumatic experience in a person's life occurring before the age of 18 that a person remembers as an adult." Schools throughout the United States use ACE scores to help teachers provide extra resources and empathy to those students with high scores. There are nine ACEs: physical abuse, sexual abuse, emotional abuse, mental illness of a household member, problem drinking or alcoholism of a household member, illegal street or prescription drug use by a household member, divorce or separation of a parent, domestic violence toward a parent, and incarceration of a household member. My score is fairly high: six out of nine, which I suspect is reflected in my strong drive toward perfection as described by Brown's continuum of perfectionism. Since my perfectionism is further along the continuum, my work requires a deeper level of healing. One hypothesis I have is that individuals with high ACE scores experience more severe pregnancy sickness.

A child dealing with a high ACE score must come up with ways to emotionally, and sometimes even physically, survive. Some of these coping strategies make sense and others may not. The child only does what they are capable of doing within the limits of their developing brain. What works when a child is young often fails them as they grow older. Part of the healing process is recognizing one's convoluted coping mechanisms, disengaging from them and creating newly functioning ones. Perfectionism is one such coping mechanism that serves to cover up the overwhelming feelings a person was unable to handle as a child.

Perfectionism allows a child to control their behavior, even saving the child from abuse at times. Other times the perfectionism has no effect on preventing further abuse, but it is the best coping mechanism available to the child in that moment. What begins as a coping behavior slowly develops over time and becomes part of the child's personality, laying the groundwork for a lifetime struggle with perfectionism.

Manufacturing moments of control was the focus of my childhood. HG came to me to help unlock this pattern, which played out when I demanded food as soon as I realized I had a craving. I think this spoke to the amount of control I was trying to recapture in my situation. Growing a baby means something is inside you, and there is not much control over when it comes out. This loss of control is similar to what happens to individuals when they are sexually abused.

As a person begins their journey of recovery from trauma, they must look around to ensure they are in a safe environment. One result of having grown up with a lot of trauma is we surround ourselves with drama and other unhealthy people. As we heal, we need to redefine our boundaries by tearing down our walls and rebuilding them. This often involves letting people go, sometimes very close people, from our lives. We have to develop strict boundaries with those who hurt us, learning how to differentiate between healthy and unhealthy people and situations. Redefining our boundaries with our self, others and our environment is vital to healing from perfectionism.

I remember the terror I felt in my body when my therapist suggested I tear down my walls and build them back up again. I pushed away from being in my body and went into my habitual place of comfort—my thoughts. *Who will I be? How will I survive being so raw and vulnerable before I build myself back up again?*

My healing path has been a long process. With the major dysfunctional people mostly out of my life or kept at bay by strong boundaries, I can more easily stay calm and grounded and more quickly distinguish when I have an issue at hand from when someone is projecting their stuff on to me and using me as a dumping ground. My daily struggle is how to respond to everyday mishaps instead of reacting to normal situations as disasters. Removing dysfunctional people from my life was challenging at times, but not as difficult as reprogramming my body and mind to realize I am no longer living in a daily crisis, needing to be in constant alert mode.

Watching how I have unfortunately passed this panic on to my kids is sometimes painful, yet at other times I have found a place of gratitude that we are working through it and healing a long-standing dysfunctional pattern that has been disrupting my family for generations.

Our family has open conversations about it and I love when my daughter chides me, "Mom you are reacting and not responding."

"Thank you so much! You are so right!" I respond, so grateful for the cue to step back and "Breathe In Respond, Breathe Out React."

"Why are you not mad at me for saying that?" she questions.

"It is exactly what I teach you and I am so glad to hear you are listening. We all need reminders when we veer off our healing paths."

"Whatever, enough of your spiritual talk," snarls my daughter as she stomps off.

When you discover pain from the past, there may be a lot of shame and desire to make it go away quickly. However, we are all a work in progress and the only way is through our stuff, not around it. My parents did the best job they were equipped to do with they tools they had, just as I am doing the best I can do now as a parent. Yet we all make mistakes and cannot be expected to handle all the mistakes and pain from the previous generations in one day, one year or even in one lifetime. We have to do a little at a time. When we try to do a

360 degree turn too quickly, we risk transferring our perfectionistic tendencies into our own healing journey by trying to do it all right now.

Confronting HG gave me the opportunity to have people care for me, be vulnerable and learn how to have faith and become comfortable with the absence of absolute answers. Earlier I mentioned trying to win a "game" and what I really was trying to win was the healthy love and affection I failed to receive as a child. On one level, I had to be open to being vulnerable while allowing myself to experience all the pain I had not been able to safely feel during childhood. In chapter 7, I elaborate on how surprisingly thankful I am for HG and the lessons I learned, most importantly how to address physical adversity as an opportunity to thrive.

7

Adversity as a Gift

Now more than fifteen years later I can finally say thank you to HG. Gratefulness is probably not the first word that comes to most people's minds, especially to HG survivors. If someone had told me my search for answers to the horrors of HG would involve a thank you, I would have probably screamed at them and then started laughing at the unfathomable idea. The HG, however, was the beginning of a long, arduous journey filled with unexpected lessons that birthed my soul in so many spectacular ways. If I had not been challenged with HG, I can only imagine what other struggles may have been placed before me and how I may still be living in daily fear, spinning my wheels, burdened by my past childhood abuse, still addicted to Diet Coke and falling victim to repeated cycles of abuse from the generations before me.

For me, HG was a gift—rescuing me from depression, anxiety, chronic pain and domestic violence, as well as encouraging me to heal from sexual abuse, teaching me how to develop healthy boundaries, giving me a reason to leave the rat race and find balance, helping me solidify my career as a writer, pushing me into a healthy diet, providing me the courage to explore midwives and distance myself from Western medicine, and introducing me to the concept of adversity as a gift.

Without HG, I am not sure I would have ever let go of my depression, anxiety and diagnosis of bipolar II. I would spend days in bed not wanting to do anything and when I finally mustered the motivation to venture beyond my bed, I would have a panic attack. Suicidal thoughts consumed me for years, yet I could never bear the thought of death, so I was stuck wanting to die but too terrified to try. For endless hours, I would stare at the razor against the white porcelain bathtub, eager to touch it and horrified that I could not dig up the courage to end my misery—stuck in immense, overwhelmingly heavy pain.

Because I was raised with so much discipline, I still showed up for work and school, though I barely survived unscheduled moments, alternating between states of being mute and curled up in a ball with fits of uncontrollable crying spells lasting for hours. Giving up the thrill of hypomanic episodes, which are intense, unexpected rushes of wild, creative energy, has taken some getting used to, but I still experience the edges of the hypomanic ecstasy when my creativity flows. The episodes were better than any drug I have ever tried and extremely helpful in cleaning up the months of the non-action during the depths of depression. Now I find I do not need the hypomania anymore, for those bursts of otherworldly energy that are practically indescribable and impossible to replicate. Since my mind is still programmed from many years of depression and anxiety, I struggle at times to maintain my center; nonetheless I am much more settled and ready to discover the routine joys I have been missing for so long.

For generations, mental health issues have run rampant through both sides of my family and Rob's family. Fortunately, Rob and I are choosing to break the generational pattern of these mental health challenges, which include a plethora of mental health issues: schizophrenia, bipolar, depression, anxiety, PTSD, and suicide. We still struggle the most with the anxiety piece that continues to surface at times in our family. We can see all too clearly how the children are developing anxious patterns, yet we are hopeful our open dialogue and alternative treatments are working as we sort out patterns that will hopefully only leave remnants of anxiety for our grandchildren.

Surviving HG woke me up to the denial that had been status quo for my family for too long. As I confronted the patterns of domestic violence and sexual abuse that have silently plagued my family for generations, I realized the HG had come through me as a message to change how I was living and how I had been falsely taught was acceptable to live. As a result, I had to relearn boundaries as a parent, starting after the birth of my first daughter.

I remember taking long showers each night during the first month postpartum—finally realizing I existed. Before my first daughter was born, I was bewildered how people could indulge in extended periods of self-care and enjoy it. My roommate used to take restorative bubble baths with candles. Intrigued by this idea, I attempted this simple task without success; unable to sit still, I just ended up envying his ability to relax. Ever since I became a mother, it is all I yearn to do. Even though I had started to implement some self-care strategies as a mother, I was still conflicted about how long to nurse, and where I ended and my children began, leading me to nurse while going to the bathroom so I would not disturb my sleeping baby. Forgetting about myself again, I even nursed through HG so I could tandem nurse my two girls.

As a child, I was unable to develop healthy boundaries because I was surrounded by people who had violated me with physical, emotional and sexual abuse. Physically and sexually I was lost because there was so much suppression around these violations. I tended to let others continue to abuse me in these areas as I grew into an adult. Within my immediate family, my role models for developing emotional boundaries were to hold your emotions inside until you exploded or dissociate and use denial. There was so much I never had the opportunity to learn, and my children were here to teach me the valuable skill of healthy boundaries. As I grew into motherhood, I became better and better at listening to the messages they were here to deliver.

Not only did I redefine boundaries between my children and me, I started to look at everyone around me, initially recognizing the dysfunction in my first marriage, prompting me to leave Dimitri. Slowly I examined other relationships in my life—questioning why my friends always let me down and seemed so concerned with themselves and wrapped in a mess of problems. Instead of welcoming every person in my world, I began to choose to whom I related and not let in people who sucked energy from me.

As I explored my relationship with my environment, I learned how spending so much time at home with HG served me well. As a new writer, I am recognizing how much I love working from home. Having grown up in a tension-filled home, I had tricked myself into believing I always needed to travel—failing to realize how much I was trying to escape my reality and inner pain. Staying close to the safe and welcoming home I have created feeds my soul in such wonderful and satisfying ways.

This illness also required me to take a deep look at my career aspirations. The state of California had approached me after my first HG pregnancy, encouraging me to open my own agency to serve adults with developmental disabilities. I was intrigued and seriously thought about it, but feared if I had HG again, the agency would probably not survive its start-up phase. Again HG pushed me to stop and think about my choices and in the end set the stage for me to leave the corporate world of social services (yes, that oxymoron actually exists and could be a whole other book)—recognizing that when something throws you down repeatedly, there is a message trying to come through.

As I look back, I can now see how the HG experience started to create the writer in me and how I unconsciously absorbed many writing skills by reading a book a day, giving me the space to create my parenting theory with my first book. HG required me to stop, look within and detoxify physically and emotionally so I could birth myself as a writer.

Examining my nutritional intake, most importantly letting go of NutraSweet, has been crucial to maintaining my emotional and physical center. HG also guided me to midwives, giving me the final confidence to birth at home after Western medicine had failed me. The midwives educated me about the importance of herbs and eating whole foods. If I had held on to the misguided ideas of Western medical care I would have ignored my own body, continuing to believe the disempowering doctors. As my boundaries and balance have increased, I have been able to incorporate both Western and alternative therapies, being careful to evaluate the fear-based, spoon-fed scientific information while remaining focused on my intuition.

Although I remain cautious of Western medicine, I am grateful for the IVs, potassium and anti-emetic medications provided during my HG pregnancies.

Some may question how I can connect the physical symptoms of HG to someone's internal world. My understanding is emotional struggles unleash biological interactions in our bodies, resulting in the manifestation of physical symptoms. In my experience the longer the symptom is present, the harder it is to alter with alternative therapies. Scientific evidence is now surfacing about how our diet and emotions turn on certain genes in our bodies, leading to illness.

In support of the crux of alternative therapies, Sharon Vogiatzi from betterthansurviving.me, blogs:

> "As strange as it sounds, you should be thankful to your disease for pointing out that something is wrong and that you need to change. If you don't make the necessary adjustments, the disease will keep coming back, no matter how many drugs you take or operations you have. Until you let go of the control, shame, anger, fear, resentment, blame, or whatever it is that's eating away at you, you will not heal. Thankfully, a good homeopathic remedy will allow your mind to expand and your attitude to shift so that you will adapt to a healthier way of thinking, thus making it easier for you to change. The remedy will also relax you and allow you to finally accept yourself for the way you are, causing the guilt and shame you've been dragging around to dissipate."

We all need to find our specific "homeopathy" path whether that is through classical homeopathy or another treatment modality or just plainly looking within. Louise Hay, founder of the self-help movement, pioneered the concept in the 1980's that your body speaks to you when it is sick, trying to alert you to change your thinking patterns. HG taught me firsthand how illness is connected to your thoughts and past experiences.

Healing from HG or another chronic illness is not a clear-cut path. When stuck with a chronic medical condition, people often search for concrete answers to satisfy their minds. Often it is necessary to question our role in the situation, examining which thoughts and behaviors are allowing this illness to be comfortable in our bodies. To wrestle with our role, we frequently need alternative healing techniques to open us to our unconscious thinking patterns. Pinpointing what and how something works can be difficult. As we heal, we learn to trust that we do not need to be in the utmost control and how letting go creates powerful conditions for healing.

When an illness is not cut and dry in terms of diagnosis or treatment, it is time to consider emotional causes. Feeling nauseous is an emotional expression of fear according to Louise Hay. What are you afraid of? As for vomiting—what are you trying to eject? What trauma is now ready to be processed by you and ejected from your body? This is not time to beat yourself up or shame yourself, but a time for tender, honest reflection. It was necessary for you to hold these experiences inside of you until you were in a place where you could let them go.

Although your life may not feel or be safe at the actual moment, especially if you are in a domestically violent relationship (refer to Appendix E: *Domestic Violence Resources*), chronic conditions are a wake-up call to change something you are doing and to uncover what needs further processing—think of disease as a conversation starter with the soul. This can be an overwhelming process, yet promises to be a life-changing proposition that slowly unfolds one step at a time. Once you journey on this path, watch how fortuitous people and ideas come into your life and open to the discovery that awaits you.

Krystal Alexander-Hille, discussed in her article, *New Perspectives on Morning Sickness*, how we may be conditioned to feel morning sickness especially because it is a supposed sign of a healthy pregnancy and thought to be a protective mechanism for the fetus. Also, she points out, like Vogiatzi, disease is just dis-ease and a sign that something is emotionally or spiritually wrong. She talks about how she had absolutely no morning sickness in her first pregnancy. During her second pregnancy, she began to experience the edges of mild morning sickness, feeling dizzy and almost nauseous. Attempts to change her energy failed; she simply could not visualize it away so she had to lie down and examine what was going on with her, realizing that she was hurrying to get out of the house. She points out how Sunni Karll, author of *Sacred Birthing*, postulates morning sickness is because the mother's vibration is not in alignment with the baby's soul. Alexander-Hille believes this happened to her since she had been rushing to be on time and "needing to be perfect" when she had initially felt unbalanced.

Now I know this seems outrageous to those of us who spent so much time being incredibly sick and doubt this would work immediately with someone with HG. But I do believe part of the answer for healing HG is in this process. Alexander-Hille also talks about the way her baby was communicating with her, and this was the only way the baby knew how to do it was by making her mother sick. Pregnant women today in the West are so much more distracted than ever and unable to connect with their babies in utero. I find it intriguing that indigenous cultures rarely report morning sickness—perhaps this is because their lives are more earth-centered and naturally grounded without the added stress and disconnectedness of industrialized nations.

Surrendering to my soul's work of birthing children with HG pregnancies was not easy, but felt like a calling—saving me from chronic illnesses that manifest when we fail to listen to our calling. My life has taken many detours, setting me up for a life of mental health diagnoses, and the struggles of chronic fatigue and fibromyalgia. Healing my HG through the pregnancies pulled me out of those illnesses.

With the gift of HG, I have shed my identity of a person who struggles daily with mental health issues and chronic pain, shedding generations of destructive patterns while deepening my knowledge of alternative medicine and enhancing my nutrition, spirituality, love, joy and creativity in this life. Now I have embraced that life is full of messages and how everything, especially the most difficult struggles like HG, are a blessing.

8

Practical Tips and Healing Techniques

The following chapter includes preparation ideas to implement when you receive a positive pregnancy test, healing techniques to try while you are pregnant, including daily practices vital to my recovery, and information I wish I had known about during my first HG pregnancy.

Take a look at the *Symptom Meaning Checklist* to discover possible connections between your symptoms and your thoughts. Use the blank chart to create a personalized list of thoughts and feelings that might be adding to your HG symptoms. Pregnancy sickness can be tough, especially when you have HG, and you cannot survive it alone so refer to the *Angel List* to gather names and contact information for those around you who may be willing to lend an extra hand. Post it on your front door with a pen attached.

I understand each pregnancy sickness experience is unique and will require an individual treatment plan. For me, each time a technique failed, I felt utter despair about how I could survive another moment of this wretched condition. This profound discouragement prevented me for so long from trying techniques that had been unsuccessful in the past. However, it was crucial to reintroduce techniques that had failed in the past in order to find a resolution. Even in my last pregnancy, healing methods would work one week and then not work so well the next week. When I finally mixed and matched techniques, I got results.

Preparation Ideas

Ask for Guidance in Your Dreams and Pray. Your dreams provide a powerful place for you to work out problems here on Earth. Ask specifically to be guided in your dreams about how to have a pregnancy free from nausea and vomiting. Praying is also a useful practice.

Freeze Meals. Freeze portions of each meal for when you may need them.

Gather Items by Your Bed. Collect books, resources and games by your bedside. Decide if you want a cooler for snacks in your room. Think about what else may be helpful to have on hand, such as tissues, baby wipes, bowls, a water bottle, and a phone charger.

Make a Support Plan. Do this as soon as you become pregnant if you do not already have one in place. Write down the potential help you might need, (i.e. childcare, grocery shopping, cleaning). Write a list of your friends and relatives and start asking for help (refer to the *Angel List* in end of this chapter). Let your key supporters know you are pregnant and you may need help soon. Some people like to host extra play dates now so, if needed, they can ask for the returned favor in the next several months. If possible, hire someone for whatever tasks remain. We hired someone from Craigslist and explained the situation upfront, telling her she would need to watch the kids and clean the house at the same time.

Mantras. Decide what mantras you want to say to yourself, saying them throughout the day. Try "Breathe In Faith, Breathe Out Doubt, "Breathe In Rest and Love, Breathe Out Guilt and Shame" or make up your own. You may even want to set a timer and say them 10-300 times every hour.

Mayan Abdominal Massage. Start relaxing your diaphragm now to prevent nausea. Refer to Mayan Abdominal Massage under *Healing Suggestions* later in this chapter.

Phone List and Schedules. If you do not have a phone list of emergency contacts, teachers for your child, and other frequently contacted people, make one now and post to your refrigerator. Post a household schedule if there is not already a schedule in place that is easy for others to manage.

Purchase Remedies. Gather remedies you want to try, such as barley tea and medical marijuana. Fill out the *Future Healing Techniques* in the end of chapter 9 with methods you think will alleviate pregnancy sickness.

Stock Up on Paper Products. Buy paper plates and cups to reduce the amount of dirty dishes. I know this is environmentally unkind, but I feel there are times you need to give yourself a break and not always do the right thing (remember, many of us working on breaking perfectionism). I was resistant to do this, and then realized this was another way I was depriving myself and trying to be perfect. Give you and your family this break.

Tie Up Loose Ends at Home and Work. Pay bills if possible. Do some extra cleaning. Try to leave work projects in a state that others could easily take over.

Daily Tips to Lessen Pregnancy Sickness

Acupressure Points. In the next section, there is a list of specific points in the Acupressure/Acupuncture Points section under *Healing Suggestions.*

Barley Tea. This Korean remedy for nausea is high in fiber and minerals. Taking small sips throughout the day was extremely beneficial in my last pregnancy.

Eat a High-Protein Diet. During the first trimester of my last pregnancy, I ate virtually no carbohydrates, engulfing a high amount of protein every morning, such as three hot dogs and three hamburgers. Karll, in *Sacred Birthing,* advocates a high-protein snack before bed, such as nuts, to alleviate pregnancy sickness upon waking. On *Raising Arrows* blog, Amy suggests drinking a casein (a slow release protein) shake in the middle of the night to prevent nausea in the morning.

Hypnosis. If you have learned self-hypnosis, this is a good daily technique to do. Refer to Hypnosis under the *Healing Suggestions* for more information.

Rest and Reduce Stimulation. You are working hard growing a baby in addition to the added stress of pregnancy sickness, so give yourself a break as much as possible. Thank yourself, instead of feeling guilty, every time you spend time by yourself resting. If you have to keep a close eye on a little one, do it as much as possible from lying down. The little ones like it better anyway when you are closer to the ground.

Self-Massage. Loving yourself as much as possible is crucial. Touch your hands and feet and thank them for being a part of you. Thank each organ for sustaining you and remember to do daily massage on your diaphragm. Refer to Mayan Abdominal Massage under the *Healing Suggestions* section of this chapter to learn how.

Stay as Hydrated as Possible with Snacks on Hand. Trying to stay hydrated is tricky. Once you are dehydrated you fall in to a vicious cycle, causing more nausea because of the dehydration. Drinking a few small sips of liquid every hour can be helpful. Here is a rehydration drink recipe: 4 cups of water, juice from 2 lemons, ½ teaspoon of sea salt, ½ teaspoon of baking soda, about 2 tablespoons of honey and if easily available, add 1-2 tablespoons of liquid calcium and magnesium. Some people have a cooler by their bed so they do not have to get out of bed to get something to eat, shielding them from refrigerator and kitchen smells that may exacerbate their nausea.

Take Prescribed Medications or Daily Remedies. Keep medications and/or remedies by your bedside if it is safe to do so. If you have little ones, you may want to keep them in a lock box by your bed. I imagine these to be anti-emetics, vitamin supplements, medical marijuana, and/or homeopathic remedies.

Visualize. Imagine feeling free from nausea and vomiting in whatever relaxing scene that comes to mind. Then visualize different parts of your body working together to make this happen.

Healing Suggestions

Many of the following techniques were crucial to my healing from HG and are useful to alleviate pregnancy sickness and helpful to use for long-term healing. Remember to mix and match techniques—what worked last time might disappoint the next time, and techniques that have failed in the past might provide relief in the future. For support people reading this book, please consider incorporating these modalities into your treatment of these hard-working mamas, and check in with them regularly about how their remedies are working. Let me know what worked for you: jen@spiritualgiftinstitute.com.

Acupressure/Acupuncture Points. Chinese medicine explains vomiting as rebellious qi: energy that is flowing in the wrong direction. With pregnancy sickness, the qi moves upwards when it should be moving downwards, it is as though the body is rebelling against something—perhaps abuse and control that was misplaced at some time in a person's life. Nausea is explained as stagnant energy in the liver, an organ which accumulates anger. In my opinion, nausea is due to unprocessed anger that has been left to fester in the liver.

The first six points listed are the ones I used during the first trimester of my last pregnancy. The last point listed is the *Triple Warmer Point*, which I discovered somewhat on my own how valuable this was to help with overstimulation—my toughest challenge in overcoming my nausea.

Placement for these points is simple to learn through the Internet. Search the name of the point, such as Stomach 36, on the following website: https://theory.yinyanghouse.com/ for point location.

I believe HG requires you to take healing into your own hands and that acupuncture for this specific illness is relatively easy to implement. I have learned to insert needles in myself and take them out; even my older kids have learned to remove them from those difficult places to reach. Going to an acupuncturist every other day may exhaust you and be cost prohibitive. However, there are community clinics sprouting up that cost only $15 per visit, making it more viable, especially if you only need acupuncture in the beginning of your pregnancy. Refer to *Appendix C: The Wonders of Acupuncture* for more information.

The following points respond well to acupuncture and acupressure, which involves placing firm pressure on these points for 1- 20 minutes. As Miriam Erick highlights in *Managing Morning Sickness*, the Exeter study found there was an equal reduction in nausea when either toothpicks were held in place or needles inserted in these points for 15 minutes. To locate points, feel around for where there is a slight depression, which may be tender.

Conception Vessel 12: Located about 4 finger widths down from the bottom of the sternum in the center, top of the abdomen.

Pericardium 6: This point is located 4 fingers widths from the wrist crease in the center of your inner forearm. This point is most known for relieving nausea.

Spleen 4: This point is located on the outer side of the foot about 2 finger widths from the bottom of the pinky toe where the two colors of skin meet.

Stomach 33: This point is located on the outer part of the upper leg about 3 finger widths above the kneecap.

Stomach 36: This point is located on the outer, lower leg about 4 finger widths below the kneecap.

Stomach 44: This point is located at the base of the second toe on the outer edge closest to the third toe.

Triple Warmer Point: This point is located 4 finger widths above the wrist on the top, center of the forearm, opposite the popular nausea point, *Pericardium 6,* on the inner forearm. This is a wonderful point to relieve you when you are feeling overwhelmed, overstimulated by the environment or nauseated. This point was particularly helpful the few times I left the house during my HG pregnancies and a fabulous tool for handling the non-HG pregnancy sickness of the last pregnancy.

Biofeedback. This is similar to hypnosis in that individuals learn to control their physiology. In biofeedback, external feedback is used to measure physiological changes, such as changes in breathing rate, and in hypnosis, changes are measured from within the person.

Chakra Balancing. There is a color associated with each chakra that follows the sequence of the colors of the rainbow, starting with red for the first chakra, following to violet for the last chakra: the crown chakra. Visualize the colors of your different chakras. If you are unfamiliar with chakras, you can Google it for lovely images of the color and location for each chakra.

Chi Nei Tsang. This powerful massage technique focuses on healing the abdomen and realigning your internal organs. Our health begins in our gut, and when our abdomen is too tense, digestion and the absorption of nutrients is disrupted.

Cranial Sacral Massage. This subtle massage involves gentle manipulation to realign the bones and alleviate stress in the skull, spine and pelvis.

Dietary Recommendations. Protein, protein and more protein! For breakfast, eat protein only, no carbohydrates. Before bed, have a high protein snack, as nuts. Avocados blend well in a yogurt smoothie and are an excellent source of fat, potassium, and magnesium. I know this recipe might not be a favorite for everyone, but I will provide it anyway. Blend 1 cup of milk or milk substitute, such as rice milk, 1 ripe avocado, ½ cup of yogurt and 3 tablespoons of honey.

Emotional Freedom Technique (EFT). This is a gentle tapping sequence that reprograms the acupuncture meridians in your body. Refer to EFT-Tom.com to learn how. Search YouTube for "Tapping for Nausea and Vomiting."

Eye Movement Desensitization & Reprogramming (EMDR). This is a simple, yet powerful trauma release technique that many therapists use. If you are a DIY person, you can do it with a friend. Think about a past trauma and rate how much it bothers you on a scale of 1 to 10. Imagine your feelings in this past situation as you move your eyes only (not your head) back and forth, following the index finger of your friend as it moves slowly back and forth in front of you at eye level. Follow the finger with your eyes for 30-60 seconds. If you begin to cry that is a good sign of release; let it flow. Discuss what came up for you afterward and rate your trauma again. It may be reduced or remain the same and lessen as you integrate the work during the week. The process helps the left and right sides of your brain communicate with each other. During trauma, we lock into the dominant side of the brain and do not process the whole picture.

Find a Support Person. Whenever you have severe pregnancy sickness, you are too sick to go to a support group, but you still need one. Check out Facebook groups, such as *Preventing Hyperemeseis Gravidarum*, *Hyperemesis Gravidarum HER Foundation* or the much larger *Hyperemesis Gravidarum* Facebook group. These groups provide a tremendous amount of social and informational support.

Gratitude. Say five things you are grateful for each night before going to bed. This is a simple, yet remarkably effective method to change your inner thought patterns.

Helicobacter Pylori (H. Pylori). One medical cause of HG is H. Pylori, which is a bacteria that causes ulcers in people. Many people who have H. Pylori are asymptomatic. Some HG mothers report an absence of pregnancy sickness after being treated for H. Pylori. Often antibiotics are prescribed, many of which are unsuitable during pregnancy. One natural solution is to consume raw garlic, which may be particularly challenging with severe morning sickness. Check out the Pink Stork for more natural healing ideas.

Homeopathy. This energetic healing method works on the belief that like cures like. Homeopathic remedies are some of the most widely prescribed medicines worldwide. The remedies disrupt energetic connections and strengthen a person's energy field. Search "Homeopathy" on the website, www.hyperemesis.org, and look for April 18, 2013 post for a list of remedies.

Hypnosis. This healing method can provide a deep state of physiological relaxation by decreasing arousal in the sympathetic nervous system. The process involves imagining pleasant imagery or reframing an experience and focusing on relaxing muscles, such as the stomach and the throat. Some HG survivors, even Kate Middleton, have reported success with this technique, which is one of the most researched alternative techniques that has been used successfully with HG for over fifty years. Researchers have had positive outcomes with as little as three to four treatments. Some researchers believe pregnant women are particularly open to this technique because when they are pregnant they seem to be more in touch with their unconscious process and willing to change before their baby arrives. I used it in the first pregnancy with minor success. Just leaving the house seemed to counteract its effectiveness. Finding someone to come to your house may be more healing. I found hypnosis to be more effective in between pregnancies to clear past trauma. Also, self-hypnosis is a possibility. Check out this book to learn how: *Self-Hypnosis: How to Master Self-Hypnosis for Beginners with Actual Scripts.*

Magnesium Sprays. Researchers have found a lack of magnesium increases nausea because of its interaction with vitamin B6, which is often low in women with HG. Vitamin B6 appears to enhance the transportation of magnesium into cells. These low magnesium levels may then in turn deplete potassium. Black beans, pumpkin seeds, avocados, and bananas are high in magnesium. Be careful with beans and bananas because they are higher on the carbohydrate side. You can buy a magnesium spray online from Vitacost or make your own. Here is a recipe: Use a glass or ceramic (no aluminum) container, such as a glass measuring cup, and pour ½ cup of boiling distilled or filtered water over 8 ounces of magnesium flakes. Eight sprays of this DIY version equal 100 mg magnesium. Dosage is between 300-400 mg a day. Do not exceed 400 mg of magnesium supplements a day. Diarrhea and cramps may result with too much magnesium. I also use this as a deodorant. It may irritate some people's skin so make a weaker oil by just using 4 ounces of flakes or spray on the bottoms of your feet where the skin is less sensitive. Another option is to add 2 cups of magnesium flakes to your bath and soak for at least 15 minutes.

Mayan Abdominal Massage. A rarely discussed fact is how a tight diaphragm leads to nausea, and this technique directly relaxes your diaphragm. This wonderful massage technique is easy to learn and do for yourself. Unfortunately, there are no videos available about this technique so I will attempt to describe it. The first step to massaging your diaphragm is to oil your abdomen and put the backs of your fingers together to form the letter M. Make strokes from your ribcage toward your belly, doing 3 small strokes on each side. This is difficult to describe so I recommend finding a local Mayan abdominal massage practitioner to teach you this technique during a home visit. When this is not possible, email me at jen@spiritualgiftinstitute.com to set up a time to learn during a video call. I went for about 10 weekly visits during my last pregnancy, performing it on myself each day I did not receive a massage.

Medical Marijuana. This finally worked for me in my last pregnancy to ward off the HG. I tried smoking pot once in my first pregnancy and felt no relief. In my third pregnancy, I tried a tincture of marijuana, but since it was not specifically designed for nausea I did not experience any relief. In my last pregnancy, I used a tincture specifically formulated for nausea and I think that is why it was a useful remedy.

Network Chiropractic. This is a gentle, effective, spinal realignment process. No cracking or abrupt movement is involved.

News Fast. Limit your contact with the news because the news contains upsetting information and can lead to overstimulation. Try to give up all forms of news for a day or a week. Then give up TV or movies for a period of time. The stories in the media distract you from letting go of your own story. Remember the game I mentioned before about refraining from watching the news? Here is a refresher: Experiment with how long you can refrain from asking questions or commenting about a news story that someone mentions.

Pray. Set your intention and decide clearly what you want in whatever form works for you. We each have a unique way of connecting to something outside of ourselves, opening to it and bringing that power into ourselves. This interaction is the crux of spirituality. Find the best way for you to pray and ask for what you truly desire, trusting that life is a journey that unfolds exactly as needed.

Reduce Stimulation. Spend as much time as you can resting. Dark rooms without people worked best for me. Treat the reduction of your nausea as your highest priority. Speak up for yourself when noises, smells and attitudes bother you. If you were sexually abused, no one was speaking up for you and now is the time to do that for yourself.

Somatic Respiratory Integration. This technique allows you to reconnect with your body through breath and touch. Some therapists and Network chiropractors are trained in this.

TAT (Tapas Acupressure Technique). This is a wonderful and simple technique to create new neural pathways. Search "TAT" on https://www.youtube.com/.

Use Your Support Plan. Refer to Make a Support Plan in the beginning of the chapter under *Preparation Ideas.* Revisit your plan regularly and update when needed. Pregnancy sickness can wreak havoc in your life and referring to something concrete can help direct you to an effective healing method.

Whining Puker Blog. Look up the post: *"Preventing Hyperemesis Gravidarum: Four Women's Success Stories,"* from September 9, 2017 for a list of additional healing ideas from four different women.

Random Information I Wish I Had Known about HG

Anti-emetics. Anti-emetics may cause birth defects. If possible, hold off taking medication until at least ten weeks gestation when major organ formation is done.

Bile. When you are vomiting bile, you have gone far beyond pregnancy sickness. Now is the time to get IV rehydration. Ideally rehydration occurs before this point.

Dystonic Reaction. This is an involuntary loss of muscle control as a result of anti-emetic drugs, such as Compazine (Zofran does not seem to cause it). The doctors do not know why this occurs, and a person can take the drug for years without experiencing this side effect and then all of a sudden experience it. Benadryl is the antidote for this. You can take oral Benadryl if you start to notice this effect and then go to the ER to get a Benadryl shot and IV Benadryl.

Home I.V. Ask your doctor to prescribe a home I.V. If your insurance does not cover it, research the cost in your area and give the information back to your insurance company, who may decide to pay for it if home treatment saves them money.

Leg Cramps. These are a serious sign and an indication of low potassium. Since potassium is needed for your heartbeat, you must seek medical attention immediately.

Symptom Meaning Checklist

Below is a chart to create your own list of emotional connections and physical symptoms. Use the chart on the following pages as a guide to what may be triggering the nausea, vomiting or other pregnancy struggles. When I am able to pinpoint the unexpressed thought or feeling as a symptom arises or a thought or two before, I can often let the physical symptom go and resolve the emotional issue at hand. When I think about what I am not expressing to those around me, I can figure out where to focus to release my symptom. Look at the third column for mantras and questions to help you heal.

Symptom	Possible Connection	Mantra/Question

Symptom	Possible Connection	Mantra/Question
Constipation	I am withholding love from someone because I am mad.	Breathe In Release, Breathe Out Holding On (What am I holding on to?)
Headache	Too much is going on inside of my head without sufficient down-time. I am living in my head & have left the rest of my body, looking for logic & forgetting my intuition.	Breathe In Intuition, Breathe Out Doubt
Heartburn	I am constantly arguing with someone or about something.	Breathe In Love, Breathe Out Hurt (Who inflamed my heart and hurt me?)
Hemorrhoid	I am fixated on events happening at a specified time.	Breathe In Faith, Breathe Out Doubt (What/Who is a pain my butt?)
Nausea	I am trying not think about having to see a certain person, such as my dad.	Breathe I Am Safe, Breathe Out Fear. (What am I unable to accept? What trauma am I reliving and ready to clear?)

Symptom	Possible Connection	Mantra/Question
Pneumonia	It is the time to grieve the loss of someone/something.	Breathe In Love, visualizing each cell infused with love, Breathe Out Grief
Pubic Bone Split	My soul is ready to heal another layer of sexual abuse trauma.	Breath In Healing and Safety, Breathe Out Violation
Sinus	I am not expressing how much someone annoys me.	Breathe In Peace, Breathe Out Conflict and let someone know how irritated I feel
Vomiting	I am unable to accept some current or past reality, such as my husband just called & said he was going to work late.	Breathe In Faith, Breath Out Doubt (That I cannot survive tonight without my husband's help. What do I want to eject from my life right now?)

Angel List

If you are looking to help our family, please write your name and phone number next to the tasks you are willing to do. Offer to do them just one time or once a week for a month.

Helper	Name	Contact
Cleaning Angel		
Driving Angel		
Errand Angel		
Grocery Shopping Angel		
Library Angel		
Meal Angel		
Pampering Angel		
Playdate Angel		

9

Long-term Healing Work

This chapter includes long-term healing techniques, which are most suited to do in between pregnancies and beneficial for many chronic conditions. Never do detoxing techniques during pregnancy. At the end of the chapter, there is a blank list to fill in about techniques you want to try and the outcomes you experience. I found it extremely useful to have a list of what to try beforehand because once the HG started it consumed me, and I was unable to motivate to even shower or brush my teeth, let alone figure how to stop this overwhelming illness. In between pregnancies, experiment with the techniques in this chapter and review the *Healing Suggestions* in chapter 8 to find a treatment plan that works best for you.

When I met Cassandra after my miscarriage, she was pregnant for the second time with HG. Here was a chance to experience HG from the other side and learn how to support someone with HG. When I became pregnant again with HG, she patiently and empathetically listened without judgment and provided resources for me. Connecting with someone who had suffered through HG made all the difference because someone who has had HG understands your experience so much more than anyone else can. This understanding was so comforting and what I was longing for during my first pregnancy, leading me to my topic for my Master's thesis, urging social support for HG. She helped me stay motivated and not fall victim to my illness, which was so challenging because of how much HG zaps your motivation for anything, even lifting your head to vomit becomes a struggle.

Long-term Healing Techniques to Try in Between Pregnancies

Adrenal Support. Adrenal dysfunction is another suspect factor in HG. The adrenals glands are located on the top of the kidneys and secrete hormones to help manage stress. When the adrenals are burnt out, there are dark circles under someone's eyes. Glutamine is a supplement that supports the adrenals by rebuilding the intestinal lining for better nutrient absorption. With adrenal fatigue, supplements of vitamin B12 and magnesium are also important.

Diet. I put this under long-term healing techniques because it is so challenging to make significant changes when you have HG. Giving up all artificial sweeteners, especially NutraSweet, is the number one dietary modification I have done for my health and most importantly my mental health. There are many artificial sweeteners in diet and sugar-free items under names, such as aspartame, sucralose and saccharin. These artificial sweeteners are sneaking in to products with sugar, such as gum, so read product labels carefully. Another toxic sugar replacer is high fructose corn syrup. Try to eat mainly whole foods and few, if any, processed foods. If you do eat packaged foods, try to stick with products that have five or less ingredients.

Enemas. Coffee enemas are an excellent cleansing tool. Buy a regular enema at the drugstore and empty the contents. Boil 3 tablespoons of ground organic coffee with 1 quart of distilled water, and simmer for 20 minutes. When cool, strain and add to an enema bottle. Refrigerate the rest for the next enema. Or add ½ teaspoon of vitamin C and fill enema bottle with filtered water. You can use these once a day or once a week while detoxing.

Energy Training. I used VortexHealing, an energetic training which is similar to the well-known Reiki, yet VortexHealing is more powerful. There are numerous energetic training systems available— if you are comfortable with energy work, learning how to access Universal energy can be tremendously powerful and healing.

Enzyme Therapy. Taking enzymes with your meals will help you digest food your body has lost the ability to digest on its own. Taking another set of enzymes between meals will help your body break down scar tissue and collagen, which are holding on to toxins.

Family Constellation Work. This Gestalt-type, group experience helps you let go of generational patterns that have been controlling you and your family's behavior for generations. Therapists are doing this work across the country, and there are meetup groups that focus on this kind of work. Observe a constellation or do your own.

Inner Child Work. Visit the little child in you. Give them all the hugs and love they missed out on as a child. Be kind and forgiving to them. Stop and listen to them when you are being unkind to yourself. Think of a loving phrase to say to them the next time you criticize yourself, such as "I love you. You are safe now." Set aside a specific time each week to heal this important part of you.

Liver Cleanse. My favorite is the Polarity Cleanse, which you can google for more information. This no cost, gentle, simple and nourishing cleanse involves eating only alkaline-forming foods, such as non-starchy vegetables and fruit, sprouts and a few nuts. You start each of the seven days with an oily, liver-flush drink and drink an unlimited amount of a cleansing tea throughout the day. Another option is the liver tonic from Herb Lore recommended by an HG survivor. The liver processes pregnancy hormones, and Ann Jarnfelt-

Samisoe, an HG researcher, concluded this processing of sex hormones contributes to nausea and vomiting. If you have a lot of toxins and/or a liver that is unable to process the toxic load, a build up occurs in the liver, leading to nausea and vomiting. Also, the liver is the organ that stores anger in Chinese medicine, so explore areas in your past or present life that contain unprocessed anger.

Oil Pulling. This is an excellent detoxing tool from Ayurvedic medicine. Use about a tablespoon high quality extra-virgin olive oil or coconut oil. Swish in your mouth for 10 to 20 minutes and spit out in a trashcan to prevent clogging the sink. Then rinse with salt water.

Setting Intentions. Upon waking, set your intention for the day. Take every opportunity to set intentions, such as on New Year's Eve or for any religious traditions you may have. My husband taught me the Universe is particularly open to your wishes on your birthday.

Supplements. Vitamin B deficiency is often tied to HG. Vegetarianism is a healthy diet, but not when you fail, as I did, to take a Vitamin B12 supplement. Vitamin B12 is not available in a plant-based diet. Vitamin B6 and Unisom has worked for many people with HG. This combination is still available in Canada under the name of Diclectin, but was removed from sale in the United States after conflicting research of the safety during pregnancy. In addition, probiotics, magnesium and the adrenal gland supplements rebuild your health.

Test for Heavy Metal Toxicity. If your mercury levels are high, consider having your mercury fillings removed. If you decide to do this, you must follow a strict protocol for detoxing and use an experienced dentist. As I said, I had mine removed without reaction and do not think it made much of a difference, but for someone with high toxicity levels, I think it may be important.

Tongue Scraping. This is a simple, powerful, Ayurvedic cleansing technique. Keep a spoon in the bathroom and scrape your tongue every morning upon waking.

Yoga. Healing your chakras through yoga is powerful. Google chakra yoga poses for specific instructions.

Zen Trigger Point or Rolfing. These are two powerful massage therapies, requiring ten sessions. Both therapies involve restructuring the posture by releasing the part of the muscle, called the fascia, which holds on to emotional trauma.

Future Healing Techniques

Healing Technique   **Outcome**

10

Concluding Thoughts

HG knocked me down when I least expected it, throwing me into the most physically debilitating years of my life. However, I am eternally grateful for the healing it brought, empowering me to discover how to resolve such a mysterious condition. Blessed and relieved in my fifth pregnancy, I finally experienced that easy second trimester I had heard so many people talk about—a mere dream in my previous pregnancies.

Since I resisted writing this book for many years, I was a bit surprised how quickly this book came through me and how alive it felt in me. Whenever I met anyone with HG, I could not stop talking—it was as though my emotions were speaking to me urging me to share my experience. As author Honor Moore said, "Our stories choose us...and if we don't tell them, then we are somehow diminished," summarizing how I feel about my HG story.

As a recovering perfectionist, I tried to avoid getting caught in all the possible directions I could go, attempting to prove this or that only to end up feeling like I was regurgitating information—I just wanted to write the book I had wanted to read during my pregnancies. Therefore, I wrote about the topics I wish had been available or shared with me earlier in my journey, realizing some of the things I just had to learn on my own. When I first had HG, Facebook did not exist, so seeking information and advice was much more difficult than it is now. Even though there are more platforms to share HG information, a reliable and safe treatment has yet to be discovered.

When I finished writing this book, I began to comment in online HG groups, and I was surprised how much people still face the same struggles after almost twenty years since my first HG. From the posts, HG mothers still seem to feel rather isolated and in need of more effective care. The mothers still report ignorant doctors who seem to discard the severity of HG. In one case, a doctor advised a new HG woman to just drink water after she had been vomiting every thirty minutes in the hours after her first meal in two days, telling her that she was overreacting and was not dehydrated. Luckily, the HG moms in the group recommended she go to the ER to get fluids.

I remember feeling that alone and isolated when I was vomiting so much and the doctors seemed unsupportive. That was the beginning of a long road of discovery to find the support and care I needed with HG and other matters in my life, eventually leading to the healing of my HG by combining alternative treatments, spiritual growth and a commitment to reducing stimulation and drama that helped set the stage for the clearing of dysfunctional generational patterns.

Initial HG literature suggested an HG mother was rejecting her pregnancy. I do not necessarily believe an HG mother rejects her pregnancy; however, I think she is rejecting some current or past experience. This unprocessed rejection leads to the baby speaking up with severe nausea and vomiting to alert the mother to alter something in her life. Phyllis Klaus, author of *Your Amazing Newborn*, points out with HG there is often a psychological component that is not always easy to pinpoint. When Klaus treated one HG client with hypnosis, she uncovered that the HG mother had transferred her fears of safety to the baby because she had felt unsafe when she was abused as a child. Out of the thirty-eight HG clients she treated with hypnosis, only two had issues related to the rejection of the fetus. The rest of the clients began to understand their HG as it related to current life stress and/or unresolved past childhood sexual abuse or maternal rejection trauma. With proper resources to contemplate what changes and support are needed, HG mothers have the potential to see dramatic shifts in their pregnancy experiences.

Psychological issues, particularly issues with your mother, have often been blamed for HG. Although I do not subscribe to the claim the relationship with your mother is primarily responsible for HG, I do believe HG does highlight the fact that there are relationships that are not working in your life. For me, HG was a red flag that there was unresolved current and past psychological stress to be examined.

With great caution, I mention the much-criticized Fairweather, who is one of the most quoted researchers of HG. He described HG as a psychological issue and advocated for a restriction of visitors. Unfortunately, this involved isolating a woman in a hospital room, sometimes for days on end, withholding a bowl as a punishment if she vomited. Even in the late 1980's, this outlandish treatment was recommended in medical textbooks. This is extreme and ridiculous. I did find, however, that isolating myself at home was a great tool for learning to reset my boundaries and manage my nausea and vomiting.

Fairweather's research was done in the 1960's when society still locked away individuals with mental health issues. Now I notice a considerable change in how mental health issues are accepted. For example, insurance companies are now paying for a year of therapy without question. In 2001, it was costly, cumbersome and time-consuming to receive approval for therapy, and insurance companies denied coverage if you had ever had depression—stating that it was a pre-existing condition. Now I feel it is somewhat in vogue to take an antidepressant or share that you have struggled with anxiety or depression. I am unsure if this shift is due to more people talking about their inner struggles or that as a society we have become extremely stressed, so we are experiencing mental health struggles so much more. Since society has more readily accepted mental health struggles, I think it may be time to reexamine how mental health factors, such as ACE scores (refer to chapter 6 for further explanation), affect the severity of people's struggles with HG.

Not much has changed in the research since I reviewed it over fifteen years ago. One current literature review of HG includes many of the same research articles from my Master's thesis because the research is still extremely limited for HG. Researchers and HG mothers still seem to be having the same trouble figuring out how to specifically handle this awful phenomenon. Researchers appear to be moving away from psychological causes and gaining more awareness that social support is vital. However, I think people sometimes misinterpret the need for social support as the need for visitors. When I was disabled from HG, I needed a community that could provide direct help, more than just a passive visitor. Having an HG buddy was great, but people without HG were not that helpful unless they were providing a specific service.

One day I envision women will have access to the services they need. Ideally, there would be a person assigned to each HG mother who would cook healthy, whole foods, clean and be trained in EMDR, hypnotherapy, acupuncture and cranial sacral work. Perhaps this is a lot to ask, yet if people could learn the key points of these techniques for this specific illness, without completing extensive training to heal every possible disease, the suffering of HG women would significantly diminish. Doctors are now allowed to take abbreviated trainings for acupuncture, and I would like that to be available to HG caregivers to treat HG mothers at home.

The closest caregivers I have observed to this model are doulas, who are mostly known for their assertive and valuable care at births and less well known for their fabulous postpartum care. After my first daughter was born, I had a postpartum doula who was amazing and would sling the baby as she cooked, cleaned and answered my never-ending questions about nursing. We considered using a doula during my fourth pregnancy because of the HG, but the cost was too high. As preposterous as this might sound, my hope is that insurance companies start paying for doula prepartum care for severe morning sickness. Imagine a world in which insurance companies paid for doulas to learn EMDR and modified acupuncture to treat HG women in their homes. As naive as this wish may be, until we envision what we want in the world, we cannot manifest it.

EMDR and hypnotherapy, two of the alternative healing techniques mentioned above, heal on a subconscious level. This deep healing is what is needed when a simple solution is unavailable. Larry Goldman, a psychiatrist, discusses a case in which a woman threw up every time her mother-in-law walked in the room or called on the phone. Under hypnosis, the therapist suggested she would more effectively punish her mother-in-law if she physically felt fantastic and smiled at her every time she saw her. Using this suggestion under hypnosis reduced the woman's HG symptoms and positively altered her relationship with her mother-in-law. When you experience an illness, especially a chronic or repetitive one, a spiritual or soul issue is trying to come to the surface to resolve a generational pattern that is ready to work itself out.

If I were to do my thesis with what I know now, I would collect data about people's perfectionism with a scale, such as the Perfectionistic Self-Presentation Scale developed by Hewitt and Flett, and data about individuals with HG and their ACE score, and how these factors may predict the severity of pregnancy sickness. I would also want to collect data about the diets of HG mothers, examining the role of processed foods and vitamin and mineral deficiencies in pregnancy sickness. I know I was an unhealthy vegetarian for nine years, never once taking vitamin B12, a vital supplement needed for people on a vegetarian diet.

I would also add a question to my research about sexual assault, which is unfortunately so prevalent and silenced in our culture. I suspect there is a correlation between sexual assault and the severity of pregnancy sickness. Maybe the lucky few women (10-20% without any nausea and vomiting symptoms) are the few that have not been sexually assaulted in our culture. To further support my suspicion, I mention that indigenous cultures have less pregnancy sickness and less sexual assault.

Although I have ideas about the direction for HG research, I believe enough research has been done and that each woman needs ample support to find her own cure, while doctors need to educate themselves about HG and adopt a model that is more holistic and client centered. Western medicine is becoming more open to alternative medicine, understanding how diet plays a role in disease, and allowing spirituality to be accounted for in treatments, yet Western medicine has further to go. It fails us when trying to treat the same illness the same way in each different person without recognizing the emotional components of illness.

Finding the several gifts of this illness has helped me survive and derive power from the experience. If I had kept on going and never received the gift of HG, I am not sure I would have ever risen to the challenge of breaking the generational patterns of domestic violence, sexual abuse and mental illness, finally learning how to be safe in and with my body.

Upon reflection, I realized I was doing my soul's work to bring my children to the Earth and learn how to resolve HG by becoming more spiritual and open to alternative health practices, shedding drama as I healed internally. As I got out of my head, into my body and more in touch with my feelings, I learned how to manage my feelings to work for me and not against me. I opened to the idea that illness is a blessing and developed connections to those who believed in me, transforming adversity by extracting the valuable lessons while discarding the dysfunctional patterns.

Just as there are many causes for HG, there is no one cure. A combination of factors appears to cause HG, so it will take a unique collection of solutions for HG to resolve. HG is an extremely difficult journey, where all your energy is focused on making it through every minute, consuming the mental and emotional space required to find meaning in this intense suffering. At times, I had to throw out all this emotional talk and as one HG survivor summarized "give (my) self permission to get through it in any way (I) could." Often spiritual lessons are hard to connect to as you are going through them and so much harder under the fog, pain, and misery of HG. As a reader, whether or not you had HG, I hope you are comforted by some of my journey and perhaps inspired to carve your own healing path.

Appendix A: 52 Ideas for Pregnancy Sickness, Bed Rest and the Newborn Weeks

When your body calls you to bed, listen. Often your soul is calling for you too, screaming for you to take a break and reflect on how your life is unfolding. This time provides an opportunity to discover if you are heading in the direction you want to go. The following exercises are ideas for mothers on bed rest. They are written with an HG pregnancy in mind and end with activities to do the first twelve weeks postpartum. Some of these are good to do alone and/or with a partner. Those not actively pregnant who have an interest in DIY healing will also find value in most of these exercises.

Week 1: Learn self-hypnosis or find a hypnotherapist in your area. This is the most researched alternative technique for HG. Check out the book *Self-Hypnosis: How to Master Self-Hypnosis for Beginners with Actual Scripts* or look up techniques online. I found the above book after typing in "Free books hypnosis" in Amazon and finally learned to hypnotize myself, deeply relaxing now in less than 5 minutes.

Week 2: Learn Mayan abdominal massage. Find a practitioner to teach you at home or read the directions for Mayan Abdominal Massage under *Healing Suggestions* in chapter 8.

Week 3: Each night before you fall asleep, name 5 things for which you are grateful.

Week 4: This is usually the earliest you find out you are pregnant. Congratulations! Start freezing leftovers and stocking up on paper goods and household products. Wrap up loose ends at home and at work.

Week 5: Eat a high protein diet with virtually no carbohydrates to minimize the nausea. If you did not already learn Mayan abdominal massage and self-hypnosis, research these this week.

Week 6: You might begin to feel sleepy this week, so schedule naps, lots of relaxation time, and find a Facebook group to support you. Some groups even have a place for you to sign up for a buddy in your area.

Week 7: The nausea might be coming on strong. Rest whenever possible and if you get bored, try this exercise. Lie in a dark room. Rub your hands together to create some warmth. Place the palms of your hands gently over your eyes and think about the color black. Now tell stories to yourself about things that are black. This is called palming: it is relaxing and helpful for your eyesight. The eyes never take a break—even while sleeping the retina produces images. Do this for at least 7 minutes to clear all the images from the retina.

Week 8: Pick a mantra to say to yourself throughout the day, such as "I love myself and I am safe." If you are vomiting bile or vomiting several times a day, go to the ER for fluids.

Week 9: This week "Breathe In Faith, Breathe Out Doubt." You are a rock star, and this might be the toughest week of your life. Try to take a sip of water or Recharge every half hour.

Week 10: Review your *Angel List* of helpers at the end of chapter 8. Keep a copy by your bedside and one posted to the front door. If you cannot ask for help yourself, ask someone else to get you the help you deserve.

Week 11: Repeat your mantras and thank yourself for being such a warrior.

Week 12: You are still struggling hard. Keep trying different techniques, such as a high protein diet, acupressure, Mayan abdominal massage, barley tea, or resting in a dark room. A combination of treatments usually works the best.

Week 13: Ask someone to give you a foot massage.

Week 14: If you have any motivation, you can continue to palm each day and find your grounding cord. Imagine a gold cord connecting from the base of your spine to the center of the Earth. There is infinite energy here for you to access through your grounding cord, helping you center your first chakra. Toss all your pain and misery out of your body into the gold cord. You can access your grounding cord any time and from anywhere, even when you are not palming.

Week 15: You are doing a great job! Your body is working so hard! Consider calling an old friend or relative to have a conversation. I checked in with a lot of old friends to help pass the time during each of my pregnancies.

Week 16: You might be feeling slightly better. Take it slowly. You might find leaving bed causes you to feel much worse. Be kind to yourself. Doing nothing is okay.

Week 17: Keep a pen and paper at your bedside to write a list of possible messages you would want to put on your mirrors or car windows of what you want more, i.e. nausea-free living, a thank you, or words like community, then watch them come into your life. You can use dry-erase markers on your car windows or mirrors. Soap and lipstick also work on house mirrors. Write a message the next time you go to the bathroom or ask someone else to do it for you.

Week 18: Try doing some Kegel exercises while resting in bed. There are actually three types: vaginal, anal, and clitoral.

Week 19: Start a journal for your baby. Write the hopes and dreams you have for them.

Week 20: Learn to knit from You Tube. Knitting passes a lot of time, and you actually get to accomplish something!

Week 21: If you are not too food triggered at this point, sit quietly, close your eyes and meditate with a small food, such as a raisin in your mouth, feeling the texture. Now try this with one chocolate chip. Try a new, small food each day. You may discover a new food you can tolerate.

Week 22: Do crossword puzzles. I had never been able to do these before, but became much better with each pregnancy.

Week 23: You can also write messages and tape them to your water bottle or a glass of water. Studies show water structure changes to be more beneficial when surrounded by positive words.

Week 24: Order a *Magic Eye* book. These look like a bunch of colors on a page and when you relax, a 3-D image pops out. It is a neat phenomenon, and I think it helps to relieve perfectionism if you can do this. I could not do at first because my eyes were too tense, but with practice I learned how to relax my eyes and view the awesome images.

Week 25: Make a crossword puzzle for someone. I found these were a good way to pass the time and stay connected to people.

Week 26: This is an easy, quiet game to pass the time. Each person starts with a piece of paper and draws for 30 seconds. You can set a timer or wing it. Then rotate papers and continue drawing. Go about 6 rounds.

Week 27: Play cards. Solitaire passed a lot of time, and *Spot It!* is a fun game to play with someone.

Week 28: Watch a caterpillar cocoon unravel. The process is very grounding. Capture it or order one, and let it live on a stick in a container large enough to support a butterfly without touching the edges. Keep fresh fennel or other greens for it to eat until it cocoons. When you release the butterfly, do not touch the wings. Open the container and let it fly away on its own. Or watch the caterpillar cocoon on some fennel in your yard.

Week 29: Give yourself a facial with egg white, clay, honey, or yogurt and put cucumber slices on the eyes. Then do a gentle face massage, or even better ask a friend to do one for you. Do not touch the temples while massaging.

Week 30: Learn about Brain Gym exercises. Here are a few. Yawn while rubbing your jaw, which will stimulate cross lateral brain communication. Tug on the top of your ears when you need an energizer or cannot remember something.

Week 31: Scan your body. While closing your eyes, breathe deeply and check in with each part of your body. Relax any parts that feel tense. Tell each part how grateful you are that it works so hard without any conscious action on your part. This is a calm activity to do in bed alone or with your child.

Week 32: Try games, such as Boggle or Scrabble, to relieve the boredom.

Week 33: Google chakras. Learn about one chakra a day during this week; there are 7 major ones. Visualize a vacuum cleaner cleaning out your chakras as it goes down your spine. This is particularly important to do after you have interacted with people.

Week 34: Practice deep breathing with yourself or your child.

Breathe in for the count of 3 and breathe out for the count of 4. By the end of the week, try to work up to breathing in 8 and out 11. To add a twist to deep breathing, pause after each exhale, working up to the count of 10 between the end of an exhale and the next inhale—a particularly healing exercise for those with asthma.

Week 35: Get a seek and find book, which is a book where you look for a list of specific objects to find on each page. These books are fun to do alone or with your kids.

Week 36: Organize your photos.

Week 37: Write your birth plan. Think about what is most important to you before, during and after the birth.

Week 38: Whoever is cooking in your house, ask them to freeze extra meals or leftovers for you. Find someone to set up a meal train for you.

Week 39: Create your baby announcement.

Week 40: Is your baby here? Congratulations! If not, your baby will be here very soon! Consider staying in the house for about a month. I know you are sick of being home, but going out too soon puts you at risk for postpartum depression and takes away from important bonding with your newborn. Enjoy this special time. Many cultures have practices in place for women to remain at home for at least a month after birth.

Week 41: Spend as much time as you can with the baby connected to your bare skin. Give the baby daily massages.

Week 42: Make time for yourself every day, such as taking a long shower, so this becomes a priority as you birth yourself as a mother.

Week 43: Make a sign saying "Thank You" and place it next to your baby. Take a picture and send it to all your lovely supporters as a thank you for their support and gifts.

Week 44: Go to a mom's group this week. I went to four each week with my first daughter, and it was a fantastic way to meet moms and get out to the park every day.

Week 45: Breast infections are common and a sign you are doing too much. If your breasts start to feel inflamed, lie down and rest. If you can find a red spot on your breast, put a grated potato on it to relieve the infection. I treated many infections this way without the need for an antibiotic. Consult a health care practitioner about taking an anti-inflammatory to reduce your swelling.

Week 46: Go to a La Leche meeting. You may meet friends for life and/or gain valuable support about the mysteries of breastfeeding and parenting.

Week 47: When your baby starts crying, look at you or your partner. What are you feeling that you have not expressed? When parents authentically expresses themselves, they may find how that calms their child. If you can figure out which parent your child channels, you can open up new worlds for you and your child.

Week 48: Go to a Pilates-based postnatal class.

Week 49: Do some postnatal class exercises while your baby has tummy time.

Week 50: Make a wallet-sized card to carry with you and one for your baby. Think about how to help your baby or yourself when you are freaking out or ungrounded. Make the list now when you are calm and commit to trying at least three of the choices the next time you are stressed.

Week 51: Dance with your baby as you hold them in a sling or in your arms.

Week 52: Share these activities with another person on bed rest and check in weekly to support them.

My hope is to turn these ideas into a deck of regular playing cards with each week written on one playing card. If you or someone you know can help make that happen, please contact me or drop me a line about the book: http://spiritualgiftinstitute.com.

Blessings,

Jennifer

P.S. If our editors missed an error, please email us at editor@spiritualgiftinstitute.com, and please let us know if a listed website is no longer active.

P.P.S. Please consider writing a review on Amazon. Nothing elaborate—just a few words about your experience reading the book/your favorite part and/or the parts you found useful or inspiring.

Appendix B: The Magic of Midwives

Midwives have a wealth of knowledge and skills to normalize birth and remove the fear-based medical model. I am so grateful to my midwives for their wonderful and rarely publicized care. The midwives were curious partners willing to share their knowledge. There are so many things they taught me physically, emotionally and spiritually. Here are a few highlights:

1. My midwives did all my prenatal care at home. They were equipped to take my blood and send it to the lab for prenatal testing. Each visit they checked my blood pressure and the position of the baby. They listened to the baby's heartbeat with a stethoscope and taught my kids how to listen. The midwives did not do any internal exams unless I requested (which I did toward the end of my pregnancy to check for dilation).

2. During my pregnancy, the midwives provided a notebook of handouts about nutrition, pregnancy, and newborn care. I learned so much about how the food you eat can heal you and provide all the nutrients you need. Unfortunately, I was too sick to immediately benefit from this information, but I did incorporate this idea to heal my body from HG in between pregnancies. I read one handout over and over in disbelief that you can get all the iron you need from herbal tea infusions.

3. When my pubic bone split in my fifth pregnancy, the midwives taught my husband an easy-to-learn chiropractic technique to reset the pubic bone. I have met women who rely on doctors alone for their pregnancies and have no idea there is a simple, quick fix for this absolutely debilitating condition.

4. The midwives educated me about how to turn a breech baby at home using moxa, a Chinese treatment comprised of dried mugwort leaves, which was successful in my first pregnancy. When this did not

work in my last pregnancy, they referred me to a chiropractor who did gentle moves over two visits to turn the baby.

5. After my first full-term birth, the midwives examined my placenta and took note there was a small missing part. When I did not stop bleeding by eight weeks postpartum, they referred me to a doctor to rule out a retained placenta and to an acupuncturist to stop the bleeding. In addition, they took my placenta after each birth and made half of it into capsules for me to combat postpartum depression, and put the other half into a tincture to use during menopause.

6. Stitching is rarely needed after a vaginal tear because stitches create more damage to the skin, increasing the risk for infection when your body is fully capable of healing on its own. Each stitch creates an additional four holes in the skin. I successfully healed in two weeks, without stitching, after my first full-term baby gave me a tear as she entered the world with her fist at her head. The midwives told me to stay in bed for two weeks and keep my legs together as much as possible. This required me to take extra caution as I got up out of bed to go to the bathroom. Remaining in bed without HG was amazing. Resting in bed goes hand and hand with bonding and caring for a newborn.

7. The midwifes revealed more tricks when I birthed my boy who was over eleven pounds, and the midwives used herbal compresses on my perineum to prevent tearing.

8. When I began to hemorrhage after my fifth birth, the midwives were prepared with a shot of Pitocin to stop my bleeding.

9. My midwives came to my house every other day for two weeks after each child was born. They answered endless newborn and nursing questions, listened to my birth story, weighed my baby, and checked the size of my uterus. This was incredibly supportive and healing.

10. Here is a great baby balm recipe the midwives shared with me: drop a handful of each of the following dried herbs: plantain, calendula, and chickweed into an enamel or glass pot of boiling water. Turn off the flame and let it steep for at least one hour. Strain and melt two handfuls of beeswax into the mixture. Let cool and put in small glass jars and apply at every diaper change.

On a side note, the midwives educated me about ultrasounds and their concerns about overuse. They let me know of a case in their study group where a woman was told her baby no longer had a heartbeat, and the doctors encouraged her to do a D&C. The woman consulted with her midwives who suggested she let her body and baby miscarry on their own to prevent scarring in the uterus, so she could have a better chance of implantation in the future. The miscarriage never happened—the baby was born full term and healthy.

In another instance, my friend had an ultrasound showing her baby had a large hole in his heart and was told the baby probably would not be born alive. The baby was born full term and healthy and had no hole in his heart.

What was going on with these ultrasounds? Are they misread or was the Universe warning us not to interfere with something greater than ourselves?

Appendix C:
The Wonders of Acupuncture

Acupuncture, which divides the body into twenty major pathways, is a powerful healing system developed over two thousand years ago. The premise is energy gets stuck along these pathways and interferes with the natural functioning of the body. Treatment involves inserting a thin needle slightly below the skin, between a ¼ and a ½ an inch. Needles vary in thickness and size: for the points mentioned in this book .16mm x .25mm would work best. To order acupuncture needles, visit http://goacupuncture.com.

When trying to locate a point, such as Stomach 36 (four finger widths below the knee cap on the outer leg), feel for a slight depression in the skin. You want to avoid inserting where there is a tendon. Some movements might be painful if you move certain muscles when a needle is in place, so remain still when needles are in you.

Miriam Erick, author of *Managing Morning Sickness*, points out there originally were only 365 acupuncture points and now there are more than 1,000 points. This may seem overwhelming, however, she says most commonly only 100 points are used. When you begin using acupuncture, you will find there are points common to most patients and specific points that regularly need attention in your own body. For example, Stomach 36 is often used to strengthen me whether I have pregnancy sickness or not.

Occasionally, I saw my acupuncturist who also gave me ear tacks, tiny pin-like pads, which she placed in my ears before labor. These were immensely helpful when I pressed on them during contractions. I also highly recommend acupuncture in labor for back pain. My acupuncturist attended three of my births to perform this amazing service. Points on the back are tricky and run the risk of harming internal organs and should always be performed by a licensed acupuncturist.

Appendix D: Sexual Abuse Healing Ideas and Resources

Books:

The Courage to Heal: A Guide for Women Survivors of Child Sexual Abuse by Ellen Bass and Laura Davis is a fabulous healing guide which has a companion workbook. The authors point out even if you do not know all the details of the abuse that is okay and not necessary to ever know. The authors discuss how when someone's home is burglarized, the victim does not wait until they know all the details of the burglary before putting everything back into place.

The Sexual Healing Journey: A Guide for Survivors of Sexual Abuse by Wendy Maltz includes hands-on exercises to heal from the violation of sexual abuse, including exercises you can do with your partner.

Daily Oiling. This is an Ayurvedic technique that is very helpful for getting to know your body again after being abused. Many survivors of sexual abuse disconnect from their bodies, often neglecting it with poor grooming or constantly hurting themselves by accident. Make a 4-6 ounce mix of oils, such as extra virgin olive oil, coconut oil (melt on stovetop first), or jojoba oil. Add a mix of 10 drops of essential oils. Use a small amount to massage your full body 1 to 2 times a day.

EMDR. Refer to EMDR under *Healing Suggestions* in chapter 8.

Inner Child Work. Refer to Inner Child Work under *Long-term Healing Techniques…* in chapter 9.

Mantra. "I am safe and at home in my body."

Appendix E:
Domestic Violence Resources

My heart goes out to you. You are not alone. When you decide to leave a domestically violent relationship you must do so with a clear plan. You are at most risk when you choose to leave and need to build a support team before you do so.

Regrettably many women live with the daily fear I endured and survive with much more violence than I could ever imagine. Fortunately, domestic violence awareness has risen and some organizations, like Shalom Bayit, are even beginning to train middle and high school students about the signs of abuse and healthy relationship patterns. The training has changed from emphasizing only physical contact as a problem and educating people about how domestic violence is a pattern of controlling behavior that erodes and demeans the self-esteem and power of a person.

When living in danger, it may be necessary to locate the quick escape button present on all domestic violence websites.

The National Domestic Violence Hotline (www.thehotline.org)—resource for victims/potential victims: 1-800-799-7233 (SAFE).

The National Network to End Domestic Violence (http://www.nnedv.org) is useful for both victims and service providers: use the "Get Help" tab for victim resources.

Shalom Bayit: http://www.shalom-bayit.org.

VAWnet (www.vawnet.org) is an easy to search website with a large compilation of resources, particularly helpful to domestic violence professionals.

For Young People:
Love Is Respect: www.loveisrespect.org
1-866-331-9474 or Text: loveis to 22522

References

ACE: scores.
http://health.state.mn.us/divs/cfh/program/ace/definition.cfm.

Alexander-Hille, Krystal. "New Perspectives on Morning Sickness."
http://www.birthgoddess.com.au/2013/08/a-new-perspective-on-morning-sickness.

BabyMed. http://www.babymed.com/celebrity-baby-and-pregnancy/kate-middleton-using-hypnotherapy-overcome-morning-sickness.

Bass, Ellen and Davis, Laura. *The Courage to Heal: A Guide for Women Survivors of Child Sexual Abuse.* New York: HarperCollins, 2008.

Bevilacqua, Laura and David Goldman. "Genetics of Emotion." *Trends in Cognitive Science,* 15(9): 401-408, September 2011.

Bluestein, Jane. *Perfection Deception: Why Striving to Be Perfect Is Sabotaging Your Relationships, Making You Sick and Holding Your Happiness Hostage.* Deerfield Beach, FL: Health Communications, Inc. 2015.

Bogen, Janet Titchener. "Neurosis: A MS-Diagnosis." *Perspectives in Biology and Medicine,* 37(2): 263-274, 1994.

Brown, Brené. *The Gifts of Imperfection: Let Go of Who You Think You're Supposed to Be and Embrace Who You Are.* Center City, MN: Hazelden, 2010.

Cardaropoli, S., Rolfo, A., and Todros, T. "Helicopter Pylori and Pregnancy-related Illness." *World Journal of Gastroenterology,* 20(3): 654–664, 2014.

Ditto, A., Morgante, G., la Marca, A., and De Leo, V. "Evaluation and Treatment of Hyperemesis Gravidarum Using Parenteral Fluid with or without Diazepam." *Gynelogic and Obstetric Investigation*, 48: 232-236, 1998.

Elias, Charles. *Self-Hypnosis: How to Master Self-Hypnosis for Beginners with Actual Scripts*. United States: MoonRun Publishing, 2014.

Emoto, Masaru. *The Hidden Messages in Water*. Hillsboro, Oregon: Beyond Words Publishing, 2005.

Erick, Miriam. *Managing Morning Sickness: A Survival Guide for Pregnant Women*. Boulder, CO: Bull Publishing Company, 2004.

Gilbert, Elizabeth. *Big Magic: Creative Living Beyond Fear*. New York: Riverhead Books, 2015.

Goldman, Larry. "The Use of Hypnosis in Obstetrics." *Psychiatric Medicine*, 10(4): 59-67, 1992.

"Got Your ACE Score." https://acestoohigh.com/got-your-ace-score.

Hannaford, Carla. *Smart Moves: Why Learning Is Not All In Your Head*. Alexander, NC: Great Ocean Publishers, 1995.

Hay, Louise. *You Can Heal Your Life*. Casron, CA: Hay House, 1984.

HER Foundation. http://www.helpher.org.

Iancu, I., Kotler, M., Spivak, B., Radwan, M, Weizman, A. "Psychiatric Aspects of Hyperemesis Gravidarum." *Psychotherapy and Psychosomatics*, 61: 143-149, 1994.

Jarnfelt-Samisioe, Ann. "Nausea and Vomiting in Pregnancy: A Review." Obstetrical and Gynecological Survey, 41(7): 422-427, 1987.

Karll, Sunni. *Sacred Birthing: Birthing a New Humanity.*
www.sacredbirthing.com, 2017.

Klauss, Marshall and Phyllis. *Your Amazing Newborn.* New York:
Perseus Books, 1998.

Klauss, Phyllis. "Search for Underlying Causes." *Midwifery Today and Childbirth Education*, 35: 15, 1995.

Kondo, Marie. *The Life-Changing Magic of Tidying Up: The Japanese Art of Decluttering and Organizing.* Berkeley, CA: Ten Speed Press, 2014.

Maltz, Wendy. *The Sexual Healing Journey: A Guide for Survivors of Sexual Abuse.* New York: HarperCollins, 1991.

Martini, Betty and Hum, D. "The Connection between Aspartame (artificial sweetener) and Panic Attacks, Depression, Bipolar Disorder, Memory Problems and Other Mental Symptoms." http://www.alternativementalhealth.com.

McCarthy, F., Lutomski, J., Greene, R. "Hyperemesis Gravidarum: Current Perspectives." *International Journal of Women's Health*, 6: 719-725, 2014.

Newman, V., Fullerton, J., and Anderson, P. "Clinical Advances in the Management of Severe Nausea and Vomiting during Pregnancy." *Journal of Obstetrics, Gynelogic and Neonatal Nursing*, 22(6): 483-490, 1993.

Nutt, Amy Ellis. *Becoming Nicole: The Transformation of an American Family.* New York: Random House, 2015.

Pink Stork. https://pinkstork.com/our-approach.

Polarity Diet. http://www.weare1.us/Health%20Building.html.

Preventing Hyperemesis Gravidarum Facebook group.

https://www.facebook.com/groups/PreventHG.

Raising Arrows. https://www.raisingarrows.net/2014/08/ultimate-guide-morning-sickness-resources.

Royal College of Obstetricians and Gynaecologists. *RCOG release: Women suffering with nausea and vomiting and hyperemesis gravidarum in pregnancy 'need more support,' News*: June 22, 2016.

Simon, Eric. "Letter to the Editor." *American Family Physician*, 60(1): 60-61, 1999.

Simon, Eric and Schwartz, Jennifer. "Medical Hypnosis for Hyperemesis Gravidarum." *Birth*: 26(4): 248-254, 1999.

Vogiatzi, Sharon. "Homeopathy: Getting "Worse" Before You Get Better." January 22, 2011, retrieved from https://betterthansurviving.me.

Weil, Andrew. *8 Weeks to Optimum Health: A Proven Program for Taking Full Advantage of Your Body's Natural Healing Power*. New York: Ballantine Books, 2007.

Whining Puker Blog. http://whiningpuker.blogspot.com/2017/09/preventing-hyperemesis-gravidarum-four.html?m=1.

Ying Yang House. https://theory.yinyanghouse.com.

Epilogue

While writing chapter 7, *Adversity as a Gift*, I had my annual PAP smear that came back abnormal. An appointment for a colposcopy, which is a biopsy of the cervix, came up quickly so I scheduled it without much thought. After the initial abnormal PAP results came, I had a suspicion, once again, I was going to be given a gift through an illness. Before the colposcopy results, I even told my husband maybe if I powered through writing chapter 7, somehow I could avoid this struggle because as I explain in the last paragraph, what I would write about began manifesting in my life.

The morning of my daughter's sixteenth birthday, I received a phone call from the nurse practitioner saying I had CIN 2, which is moderate dysplasia that may lead to cervical cancer. The nurse strongly recommended a LEEP procedure to burn off the top layer of my cervix. That sounded unpleasant and I had already done a little research when I had first learned I had an abnormal PAP—digging up some handouts from a class about cervical dysplasia I had taken at the Northern California Women's Herbal Symposium. I felt confident as I held the information in my hand, explaining I was going to use alternative methods to heal and would retest in three to six months.

I am on that journey now and I am scared, yet thankful to journey through another layer of healing. I am using herbs, vitamins, suppositories, yoga, self-hypnosis, crystals, visualizations and revisiting sexual abuse healing by doing EMDR and TAT.

This pattern of my writing mirroring my present experience also happened while writing about perfectionism in chapter 6, adding to my suspicion that some healing was possibly going to be needed when I received the abnormal PAP. My chronic neck, shoulder and arm pain resurfaced intensely. I believe this pain initially began as my body's first cry to let go my perfectionism, yet I continued to ignore it until my fourth pregnancy with HG. Strangely, when I was writing chapter 6, the pain would not go away with the usual massage treatment or activity restrictions. Just before my CIN 2 diagnosis, I had performed a special ritual to wish my chronic pain away. As soon as I started to do the yoga poses recommended to heal CIN 2 and my pelvic region, the chronic neck, shoulder and arm pain subsided. My wish for the chronic pain came true, yet not exactly as I had planned.

Update 12/19/2017

Nearly a year later, I received wonderful news: a clear PAP. I feel excited and blessed that I have healed another medical condition naturally. Please visit my website: http://spiritualgiftinstitute.com for more details about the techniques that worked for me.

Acknowledgements

Thank you to my healing team: Rob, Awakenings Birth Services, NCWHS, Leslie x 2, Christine, Charlene, Guy, Nancy, Miriam, Heather, Amanda, Cassie, Mom, and especially Astrid Grove for introducing me to Mayan Abdominal massage, and the fact that a tight diaphragm is linked to nausea. This was a key point in my healing which was never mentioned during my first four pregnancies with hyperemesis gravidarum.

I am forever grateful to my incredibly giving, loving and patient husband for standing by me so strongly during my HG pregnancies and his willingness to learn how to overcome this illness.

My children continue to bless me daily; I cannot thank you enough for the joy you have given me and the lessons you have taught me.

Thank you to my editor, Louise Ash, for your wonderful edits and support of my writing.

I appreciate all of you not yet mentioned who played a part directly or indirectly in my healing, the creation of this book and its launch: Renee, Judi, Nathan, Robin times two, Lisa, Camille, Emma, Julia, Shauna, Suzanne, Noam, Deborah, Linda, Sarah, Autumn, Caroline, Kristen, Jenny, Susan, Julie, Hitomi, Holly, Meredith x 2, Liza, Becky, John, Dodo, and Kit and anyone else I may have accidentally forgotten.

Call for Reviews

Reviews are important to authors and readers so please take a minute to write a short review for *Understanding Morning Sickness as a Gift* on Amazon.

Never done one before—do not worry. Here are a few possible questions to think about:

What was your favorite part?

What was most valuable?

What would you add or subtract?

Who is the best audience for this book?

Made in the USA
Coppell, TX
12 June 2022

78747322R00073